PRENTICE HALL
SCIENCE

ANNOTATED TEACHER'S EDITION
Laboratory Manual

DYNAMIC EARTH

Prentice Hall
Englewood Cliffs, New Jersey
Needham, Massachusetts

Laboratory Manual
Annotated Teacher's Edition

PRENTICE HALL SCIENCE
Dynamic Earth

ISBN 0-13-986480-6

151617–DBH–97

 Prentice Hall
A Division of Simon & Schuster
Englewood Cliffs, New Jersey 07632

Contents

Overview of the Laboratory Manual

Science is an exciting area of study for the middle school and junior high-school student, and the *Prentice Hall Science Laboratory Manual* helps bring forth this excitement through a variety of activities that are interesting and informative. The *Laboratory Manual* consists of Laboratory Investigations directly correlated to the information presented in each chapter of the *Prentice Hall Science* textbook. The varied investigations and activities review information presented in each chapter and reinforce key concepts and scientific terms in an enjoyable and creative manner.

Thus, the *Laboratory Manual* is a companion text for your students, designed to help you in the teaching of the text material. This Annotated Teacher's Edition provides all the information needed to help you perform these investigations and activities with your students. It features answers to all Laboratory Investigations, annotations for general laboratory preparations, descriptions of the annotations in the Annotated Teacher's Edition, guidelines for laboratory safety, guidelines for the use and care of animals, a comprehensive laboratory materials and equipment list, and addresses of suppliers of laboratory materials and equipment.

The *Laboratory Manual* contains only Laboratory Investigations that require a minimum of materials and equipment and that can be performed without an elaborate laboratory facility. Most equipment used in the investigations should be readily available at the school or can easily be obtained locally or through a supply house at minimal cost. In addition, the Laboratory Investigations require a minimum of preparation by the teacher, and most can be completed within a single class period.

It is strongly suggested that students be required to read the appropriate Laboratory Investigation one day prior to performing it in the laboratory. Furthermore, it is suggested that the students be asked to provide hypotheses to each problem presented in the Laboratory Investigation. You may want to write these hypotheses on the board before beginning the investigation. Then, after the students complete the investigation, go back and analyze each hypothesis. Make sure students realize that they are not being graded on their suggested hypotheses. Even scientists may discard a hypothesis after the data have been analyzed.

LABORATORY INVESTIGATION FORMAT

Each Laboratory Investigation is developed to strengthen the student's laboratory procedures, use of the scientific method, and problem-solving skills. The purpose of the Laboratory Investigations is also to provide a practical application of the material presented in the student textbook. The easy-to-follow format of each Laboratory Investigation allows the students to complete the investigations on their own, perhaps after an overview and brief explanation from you. This allows you to provide the necessary help to those individuals or groups of students who require teacher assistance. Each Laboratory Investigation is organized in the following manner.

Background Information

An overview is presented at the beginning of each Laboratory Investigation. This overview relates the Laboratory Investigation to a specific key concept presented in the student text or provides background information that the student will need in order to complete the lab.

Problem

Each Laboratory Investigation challenges the student by introducing a problem in the form of a question. Upon successful completion of the Laboratory Investigation, the student should be able to answer the initial question.

Materials

Each Laboratory Investigation contains a list of materials necessary to complete the lab. The quantity of materials necessary for each exercise has been designed for groups of students or an entire class. In general, groups of six students work best. A comprehensive alphabetical listing of necessary equipment and materials can be found on page T–13 of this Annotated Teacher's Edition.

Procedure

An easy-to-follow, step-by-step outline provides details necessary for the successful completion of the Laboratory Investigation by the students. In many of the Laboratory Investigations, drawings are included to help the students as they complete the lab.

Safety symbols are included next to those steps in the Procedure that require students to follow specific safety precautions. Students should be reminded that a safety symbol alerts them to follow appropriate safety precautions for that particular step in the procedure as well as in all following steps. For example, the first time an open flame is used, students will see the symbol of the open flame. Students should put on safety goggles for that particular step and continue to wear them throughout the investigation unless instructed to remove them.

Observations

In keeping with the traditional scientific method, Observations are asked for after the Procedure in each investigation. Observations often include filling in data tables and graphs, as well as answering general questions.

Analysis and Conclusions

Using observations and knowledge gained from reading the appropriate chapter in the textbook, students are asked to draw conclusions. Analysis and Conclusions allow students to tie together the Problem, Procedure, and Observations comprising the investigation they have performed.

Critical Thinking and Application

This section encourages students to use critical-thinking skills to answer a variety of questions based on the Laboratory Investigation and their textbook reading. Many questions emphasize possible applications of the experiment just performed and allow students to tie the investigation to real-life situations they may face or to situations a scientist might face.

Going Further

Each Laboratory Investigation concludes with a section entitled Going Further. This section provides students with additional activities to investigate, which may be used as enrichment activities, supplementary activities, or alternative activities. Complete instructions for performing the additional activities are included so that individual students can perform the activities without additional teacher help.

Safety Symbols

On page 4 are several safety precaution symbols. A short paragraph describes what each symbol means and the safety precautions to take when the symbol appears in a Laboratory Investigation. These symbols immediately alert students to the need for special safety precautions. It is suggested that you make sure students are aware of the meaning of each symbol before starting any Laboratory Investigation.

Teacher Annotations

This Annotated Teacher's Edition allows the teacher the convenience of immediate reference to answers, suggestions, and additional instructions or precautions for the Laboratory Investigations provided in the *Laboratory Manual*. The annotations are printed in red on the pages corresponding to the student pages.

The Annotations provided for the Laboratory Investigation questions are

1. Specific objective answers, such as those provided in Observations, Analyses and Conclusions, and Critical Thinking and Application.
2. Anticipated student answers based on varied student data where there is an expected response.
3. Subjective answers to those questions that may provide a variety of responses. These will be marked by the statement "Answers will vary." The teacher should look for a logical response based on the observations and data collected by the students during the investigation.

Guidelines for Laboratory Safety

Safety should be an integral part of the planning, preparation, and implementation of a laboratory program. Both the teacher and the student are responsible for creating and maintaining an enjoyable, instructional, and safe environment in the laboratory.

GENERAL SAFETY CONSIDERATIONS

Emphasis on proper safety precautions for each Laboratory Investigation is an essential part of any pre-laboratory discussion. Prior to each investigation, demonstrate the proper use of the required equipment. Demonstrate any potentially hazardous procedure used in that investigation. Always wear the required safety protective devices during the demonstrations and the investigations. If students are required to wear safety goggles, you and any visitors to the class must also wear them.

During an investigation, move about the laboratory to keep a constant watch for potentially dangerous situations. Behavior that is inappropriate to a laboratory situation should be curtailed immediately. Wild play and practical jokes are forbidden in the laboratory. Once students realize that the practice of safety is a required part of the course, they will accept a serious approach to laboratory work.

Any Laboratory Investigation a student performs should have your prior approval. Students should never work in the laboratory without adult supervision. At the conclusion of the investigation, cleanup should follow authorized guidelines for waste disposal. The laboratory should be restored to a safe condition for the next class.

CLASSROOM ORGANIZATION

Furniture and equipment in the laboratory should be arranged to minimize accidents. Assign students to laboratory stations. Each station should be equipped with a flat-topped table and laboratory bench. Do not use desks with slanted tops. Provide several locations where students can obtain needed supplies. Control traffic flow in the room to prevent collisions between students who are carrying or handling equipment. Tell students to leave their personal property in a designated location, away from the laboratory stations. Do not use the floor and benches for storage areas. Stress that good housekeeping is important in maintaining safe laboratory conditions. Students should keep all laboratory work areas clean. Unnecessary papers, books, and equipment should be removed from working areas.

Be sure that water faucets, hot plates, gas outlets, and alcohol or Bunsen burners are turned off when not in use.

SAFETY EQUIPMENT

Any classroom where Laboratory Investigations are performed should contain at least one of each of the following pieces of safety equipment: (1) fire extinguisher, (2) fire blanket, (3) fire alarm, (4) phone or intercom to the office, (5) eyewash station, (6) safety shower, (7) safety hood, and (8) first-aid kit. If any of these basic pieces of safety equipment are not available, you may need to modify your laboratory program until the situation is remedied.

Make sure students know the location and proper use of all safety equipment. Where appropriate and practical, have students handle or operate the equipment so that they become familiar with it. Make sure all safety equipment is in good working order. All malfunctions should be promptly reported in writing to the proper school or district administrator.

Fire equipment At the beginning of the school year, you may wish to give each student the opportunity to actually operate a fire extinguisher, as the sound and action of a CO_2 fire extinguisher can be quite alarming to those who have never used one. You may also want to have students practice smothering imaginary flames on one another with the fire blanket.

Eyewash station The eyewash station should be used if chemicals are splashed onto the face or eyes. The exposed area should be left in the running water for five to ten minutes.

Safety shower The shower is used when chemicals have been spilled on a student's body or clothing. The student should stand under the shower until the chemical is completely diluted. Have a bathrobe or some type of replacement clothing handy in case the student's clothing is so badly contaminated that it must be removed.

You may want to set up one or two spill kits in your laboratory. The contents of a spill kit are used to neutralize chemicals such as acids and bases so that they can be cleaned up more easily. Baking soda (sodium bicarbonate) can be used to neutralize acids. Vinegar (acetic acid) can be used to neutralize bases. Commercial spill kits for acids, bases, and a number of other chemicals are available from supply houses.

Safety hood Use a safety hood whenever students are working with volatile or noxious chemicals. Make sure that the room is well ventilated when students are using any kind of chemicals or are working with preserved specimens. Warn students of the flammability and toxicity of various chemicals.

First-aid kit A typical first-aid kit contains an assortment of antiseptics, bandages, gauze pads, and scissors. Most also contain simple instructions for use. Be sure to read the instructions if you are not familiar with basic first-aid procedures. A first-aid kit should be taken on all field trips. For field trips, you may wish to add such items as a bee-sting kit, meat tenderizer, tweezers, and calamine lotion. Do not dispense medication (including aspirin).

CLEANUP

Before beginning an investigation, instruct students in the proper cleanup procedures. Mark certain containers for the disposal of wastes and the collection of soiled glassware and equipment. Have students dispose of broken glassware in a separate trash container. Before the end of the laboratory period, have students unplug microscopes and other pieces of equipment and put them away in their proper location. Have students wash glassware, wipe up spills, and do whatever else is necessary to clean up their work area. At the conclusion of the Laboratory Investigation, the room should be restored to a clean and safe condition for the next class. You may wish to institute a policy of not dismissing the class until the laboratory area meets with your approval.

PREPARATIONS AND THE STORAGE ROOM

Reagents stored in the stockroom should be clearly labeled and stored safely. Take inventory of reagents frequently and keep up-to-date records of their use. Check local and state regulations for maximum permissible amounts of reagents allowed in school. In case of fire or vandalism, inform the authorities of possible hazards to the community. Keep all chemicals in a locked storage area that is accessible only to you or individuals under your direct supervision.

Some chemicals are incompatible and should be stored separately. For suggested shelf-storage-patterns, refer to *School Science Laboratories: A Guide to Some Hazardous Substances,* U.S. Product

Safety Commission, Washington, DC, 1984. This publication may be obtained from your state science supervisor or the U.S. Consumer Product Safety Commission, Room 412—EX-O, Washington, DC 20207. Check local and state laws for regulations on storage of flammable liquids. The National Fire Protection Association recommends that flammable liquids be stored in vented, flame-resistant cabinets. Store large containers near floor level. Make sure that storage shelves have a raised lip at the front to prevent containers from sliding forward.

HAZARDOUS MATERIALS

Some reagents can be explosive and should not be on the premises. If found, they should be removed by trained fire or police bomb squads or by other qualified officials.

Known carcinogens and probable carcinogens have frequently been found in stockrooms and should be removed by health authorities or a licensed commercial company. If you have doubts about the hazards of any reagent in the stockroom, contact an appropriate agency (NIOSH or a local health agency).

Known carcinogens commonly found in school science laboratories include the following:

arsenic powder	formaldehyde
arsenic trichloride	lead arsenate
arsenic pentoxide	benzene
arsenic trioxide	chromium powder
asbestos	sodium arsenate
benzidine	

Possible carcinogens include the following:

acrylonitrile	cadmium powder
cadmium chloride	cadmium sulfate
carbon tetrachloride	chloroform
ethylene oxide	nickel powder

Exercise great care in using refrigerators. Never store flammable liquids in a refrigerator unless it is explosion-proof. Do not store food where microbial cultures are stored. Clean refrigerators frequently and safely discard old material.

LABORATORY GLASSWARE

Probably the most common school laboratory accidents involve cuts from chipped or broken glassware and burns from hot glassware. Discard any glassware that has a crack or chip. Use only borosilicate glassware. Fire-polish the ends of glass tubing. Allow hot glassware to cool on a hot pad for several minutes before picking it up. If an accident should happen, first aid for minor cuts and burns is immersion in cool running water. For cuts that are bleeding heavily, apply pressure with folded toweling or gauze. Call a health professional immediately.

To insert glass tubing into a stopper, lubricate the stopper hole and the tubing. Wrap the tubing in several layers of toweling and gently work the tubing into the stopper, using a twisting motion and keeping the hands as close together as possible. Wear heavy gloves. Remove the tubing in the same manner as soon as possible. Tubing that is stuck is nearly impossible to remove without cutting the stopper.

To avoid unwanted cultures, clean glassware frequently by using laboratory detergent. Most deposits can be removed with dilute hydrochloric acid or sodium hydroxide solution. Do not permit students to eat or drink from laboratory glassware.

Measuring small amounts of liquids with pipettes is common in investigations. But never pipette by mouth. Use rubber suction bulbs designed for use with pipettes or pipette fillers.

SAFETY PROCEDURES WITH MICROBIAL CULTURES

Never culture pathogenic bacteria. However, treat all bacterial cultures as if they are pathogenic. Firmly seal with clear tape any bacterial plates that are used for student inspection. For sterilization, use a high-temperature gas flame rather than an alcohol burner or candle flame.

Cultures should be killed before disposal. Autoclave all cultures and contaminated glassware at 15 pounds pressure per square inch (103.4 Pa) for 20 minutes. Disposable plates should be incinerated.

SAFETY PROCEDURES WITH MICROSCOPES

Never use direct sunlight as a light source for the microscope. The lenses may concentrate the light and cause permanent retinal damage. With a soft cloth dipped in isopropyl alcohol, clean the eyepiece of each microscope between viewers. Make sure any electrical cords are out of the main traffic pattern of the classroom.

SAFETY PROCEDURES WITH DISSECTIONS

Handle sharp and pointed instruments with care. Make sure the specimen is firmly secured on a dissection tray or cutting board. Caution students never to dissect a hand-held specimen. Make sure that the scalpels and scissors are sharp and adequate for the job. If razor blades are used for cutting tissues for slide mounts, use only single-edge noninjectable blades. Dissecting instruments should not be removed from the laboratory and should be stored in a locked cabinet.

Formaldehyde has been identified as a carcinogen and mutagen. Any formaldehyde-preserved specimens in the stockroom or classroom should be removed from the school site by qualified health authorities or a licensed commercial company. Specimens are now sold in alternative preservatives. Follow the instructions on the package for preparing specimens for dissection. Most should be rinsed in running water before use. Some may need to be soaked in water overnight if the preservative is particularly strong smelling. Specimens that have not been preserved should be used sparingly and only for a short time. Use only healthy specimens. Instruct students to wear masks and gloves to guard against infection. After dissection, specimens should be discarded in separate containers that can be transported to an incineration site.

FIELD STUDIES

Before taking the students on a field study, examine the area for possible safety hazards. Look for terrain or water hazards and poisonous plants and animals. Obtain the necessary written permission from parents and school authorities. Instruct students on proper dress and behavior. Make sure that students are thoroughly familiar with the investigations they are to conduct. If students are to form small groups, decide in advance when and where they will reassemble. Do not allow any student to travel alone.

Identify any students who have special health problems, especially allergies. Alert these students to potential hazards. Be sure they are adequately prepared to deal with emergencies.

Guidelines for the Use and Care of Animals

Animals are an essential part of a science curriculum. Few things are as interesting and motivating to students as animals. The judicious use of live or preserved animals can help students realize that the study of science is relevant, fascinating, rewarding, and not merely another dull textbook exercise.

Although there are many advantages to providing students with opportunities to study real animals, it is important to be aware of, and sensitive to, ethical and practical concerns. The purpose of this section is to discuss some realistic guidelines for using animals in the classroom. The final decision regarding the use of animals in your classroom should take into consideration these recommendations, local and school guidelines, your personal views, and your assessment of your students' needs, interests, maturity, and ability to behave responsibly.

1. Whenever possible, live animals should be observed in their natural habitats or in zoos, parks, and aquaria.
2. Check the state and federal codes regarding animal welfare that apply in your area. You may also wish to refer to guidelines published by the National Science Teachers' Association, the National Association of Biology Teachers, and the International Science Fair. Make students aware of all safety rules and regulations regarding animals.
3. Before bringing a live animal into the classroom, determine whether a proper habitat can be maintained in the classroom situation. Such a habitat includes temperature, space, and type of food. Students should have a clear understanding of the appropriate care needed by the live animals brought into the classroom. Do not allow students to tap on animal enclosures or otherwise disturb the animals.
4. No wild vertebrate animals should be brought into the classroom. Purchase animals from a reputable dealer only.
5. Live animals should be nonpoisonous and healthy. Any mammals used in the classroom should be vaccinated against rabies unless the animals were purchased recently from a reliable scientific supply company. Quarantine any animal to make sure it is disease-free before bringing it into the classroom.
6. Make sure that the living quarters of classroom animals are clean, located away from stressful situations, appropriately spacious, and secure enough to confine the animal. You may wish to lock cages to prevent the accidental release of animals; the small padlocks used on luggage are good for this purpose.
7. Remove wastes from animal living quarters daily. Thoroughly clean animal living quarters periodically to ensure that they are odor- and germ-free. Provide a daily supply of fresh water and any other need specific to the particular animal.
8. Provide for the care of animals during weekends and school vacations. Inform the custodial staff of the presence of animals and warn them of any special requirements. For example, turning off the aquarium pump to save electricity or spraying the classroom for insects can be fatal to animal collections.
9. Students should be instructed as to how to handle each species brought into the classroom. For example, students can receive painful wounds from the improper handling of some fishes, mollusks, and sea urchins.
10. Animals should be handled only if necessary. If an animal is frightened or excited, pregnant, feeding, or with its young, special handling is required.
11. Students should thoroughly clean their hands after handling animals or the cage containing animals.
12. Animals should be returned to their natural habitat after an observation period of not longer than 14 days. However, laboratory-bred animals or species that are not indigenous to an area should not be released into the environment.
13. If an animal must be euthanized, do not allow students to watch. Do the sacrificing humanely. Contact the local humane society for advice.
14. Before performing any experiment involving live animals, check local and state regulations. In some states, certification is required before a teacher is permitted to experiment with animals.
15. No animal studies involving anesthetic drugs, pathogenic organisms, toxicological products, carcinogens, or radiation should be performed.
16. Any experiment requiring live animals should have a clearly defined objective relating to the teaching/learning of some scientific principle.

17. No experimental procedures that will cause pain, discomfort, or harm to mammals, birds, reptiles, fishes, and amphibians should be done in the classroom or at home.
18. Surgical procedures should not be performed on live vertebrate animals.
19. If fertilized bird eggs are opened, the embryo should be destroyed humanely two days before it would have hatched, at the latest.
20. Whenever possible, substitute plants or invertebrate animals for vertebrates.
21. When working with preserved animals, make sure that students maintain a serious and respectful attitude toward the specimens.

HANDLING ETHICAL ISSUES

There is much controversy regarding the use of animals in scientific research. This controversy extends to preserved animals in dissections as well as to live animals in experiments. Although the battle over what uses of animals are appropriate in a science classroom can be frustrating and emotionally charged, it can also provide an opportunity for students to closely examine a current issue. You may wish to have students read current literature on the subject and contact groups and individuals with varying points of view.

Stress that it is important to make a rational, informed decision before taking a stand on any issue. Point out that it is vital to know and understand the arguments on both sides of an issue. Help students analyze the sources they find in terms of slant, bias, and the reliability and objectivity of the author(s). Teach them to learn to distinguish between fact and opinion. Encourage them to question what they read and hear. Challenge them to discover the hidden assumptions and implications of different points of view.

If dissections are a part of your curriculum and a student chooses to avoid dissections because of ethical concerns, you should respect that student's opinion. Point out, however, that no simulation or videotape can replace hands-on, first-hand experience.

NABT GUIDELINES FOR THE USE OF LIVE ANIMALS

> **The National Association of Biology Teachers (NABT) has developed the following set of guidelines to be used when working with live animals.**

Living things are the subject of science, and their direct study is an appropriate and necessary part of science teaching. Textbook instruction alone cannot provide students with a basic understanding of life and life processes. We further recognize the importance of research to understanding life processes and providing information on health, disease, medical care, and agriculture.

The abuse of any living organism for experimentation or any other purpose is intolerable in any segment of society. Because science deals specifically with living things, professional educators must be especially cognizant of their responsibility to prevent inhumane treatment to living organisms in the name of science and research. This responsibility should extend beyond the confines of the teacher's classroom to the rest of the school and community.

The National Association of Biology Teachers, in speaking to the dilemma of providing a sound science education while addressing the problem of humane experimentation, presents the following guidelines on the use of live animals.

A. Science experimentation should lead to and be consistent with a respect for life and all living things. Humane treatment and care of animals should be an integral part of any lesson that includes living animals.
B. All aspects of exercises and/or experiments dealing with living things must be within the comprehension and capabilities of the students involved. It is recognized that these parameters are necessarily vague, but it is expected that competent teachers of science recognize these limitations.
C. Lower orders of life, such as bacteria, fungi, protozoans, and invertebrates, can reveal much basic science information and are preferable as subjects for invasive studies wherever and whenever possible.
D. Vertebrate animals may be used as experimental organisms in the following situations:
   1. Observations of normal living patterns of wild animals in the free-living state or in zoological parks, gardens, or aquaria.
   2. Observations of normal living patterns of pets, fish, or domestic animals.
   3. Observations of science phenomena, i.e., including ovulation in frogs through hormone injections that do not cause discomfort or adverse effects to the animals.
E. Animals should be properly cared for as described in the following guidelines:
   1. Appropriate quarters for the animals being used should be provided in a place free

from undue stresses. If housed in the classroom itself, animals should not be constantly subjected to disturbances that might be caused by students in the classroom or other upsetting activities.

2. All animals used in teaching or research programs must receive proper care. Quarters should provide for sanitation, protection from the elements, and have sufficient space for normal behavioral and postural requirements of the species. Quarters shall be easily cleaned, ventilated, and lighted. Proper temperature regulation shall be provided.

3. Proper food and clean drinking water for those animals requiring water shall be available at all times in suitable containers.

4. Animals' care shall be supervised by a science teacher experienced in proper animal care.

5. If euthanasia is necessary, animals shall be sacrificed in an approved, humane manner by an adult experienced in the use of such procedures. Laboratory animals should not be released in the environment if they were not originally a part of the native fauna. The introduction of nonnative species, which may become feral, must be avoided.

6. The procurement and use of wild or domestic animals must comply with existing local, state, or federal rules regarding same.

F. Animal studies should be carried out under the provisions of the following guidelines:

1. All animal studies should be carried out under the direct supervision of a competent science teacher. It is the responsibility of that teacher to ensure that the student has the necessary comprehension of the study being done.

2. Students should not be allowed to take animals home to carry out experimental studies. These studies should be done in a suitable area in the school.

3. Students doing projects with vertebrate animals should adhere to the following:

a. No experimental procedures should be attempted that would subject vertebrate animals to pain or distinct discomfort, or interfere with their health in any way. Pithing of live frogs should be carried out by a teacher experienced in such procedures and should not be part of the general class activity.

b. Students should not perform surgery on living vertebrate animals except under the direct supervision of a qualified biomedical scientist.

4. Experimental procedures should not involve the use of microorganisms pathogenic to humans or other animals, ionizing radiation, carcinogens, drugs, or chemicals at toxic levels, drugs known to produce adverse or teratogenic effects, pain-causing drugs, alcohol in any form, electric shock, exercise until exhaustion, or other distressing stimuli.

5. Behavioral studies should use only positive reinforcement in training studies.

6. Egg embryos subjected to experimental manipulation must be destroyed humanely at least two days prior to hatching. Normal egg embryos allowed to hatch must be treated humanely within these guidelines.

7. The administration of anesthetics should be carried out by a qualified science teacher competent in such procedures. (The legal ramifications of student use of anesthetics are complex, and such use should be avoided.)

G. The use of living animals for science fair projects and displays shall be in accordance with these guidelines. In addition, no living vertebrate animals shall be used in displays for science fair exhibitions.

H. It is recognized that an exceptionally talented student may wish to conduct original research in the biological or medical sciences. In those cases where the research value of a specific project is obvious by its potential contribution to science, but its execution would be otherwise prohibited by the guidelines governing the selection of an appropriate experimental animal or procedure, exceptions can be obtained if:

1. the project is approved by and carried out under the direct supervision of a qualified biomedical scientist or a designated adult supervisor in the field of the investigation; and

2. the project is carried out in an appropriate research facility; and

3. the project is carried out with the utmost regard for the humane care and treatment of the animals involved in the project; and

4. a research plan is developed and approved by the qualified biomedical scientist prior to the start of any research.

Laboratory Materials and Equipment

Note: Safety equipment has not been listed. It is recommended that a laboratory apron, safety goggles, and heat-resistant gloves be worn when required.

Item	Quantity per Group	Laboratory Investigation
Balance, triple-beam	1	9, 10
BB shot	1 package	14
Beaker		
150 mL	1	8
250 mL	1	6
	2	10
400 mL	1	4, 8
500 mL	1	8
Boiling beads, glass	1 package	14
Bucket	1	13
Bunsen burner	1	4
Chalk	2 pieces	10
Clamp		
beaker	1	4
burette	1	6
	2	14
Drawing compass	1	2
Food coloring	1 bottle	4
Forceps	1	12
Glass caster cups	3	8
Glass jars, small, with lids	12 to 16	12
Golf ball	1	1
Gravel	1 package	13
fishtank	1 package	14
Hardness kit	1	5
Hose with spray nozzle	1	13
Hot plate	1	8
Hydrochloric acid, dilute	100 mL	10
Ice, crushed	1 container	8
Jar, with lid	1	9
Knife	1	1
Magnet	1	5
Magnifying glass	1	7, 8, 11, 12
Medicine dropper	1	12
Metric ruler	1	11, 12
Microscope	1	12
Microscope slides and coverslips	1 set	12
Modeling clay, different colors	3 sticks	1
Paper cups	3	12
Paper plates	3	12
Paper towels	1 roll	8, 10
Paper, white, unlined	1 sheet	11
Paradichlorobenzene (PDB) flakes	1 package	8
Pencil, glass-marking	1	8
Plastic bags, with ties	6	12
Plastic columns with rubber stoppers	3	14
Radish seeds	30	12
Ring stand	1	4, 6, 14
Rock and mineral samples		
galena	1	6
granite	1	8
mineral set	1	5
obsidian	1	8
pyrite	1	6
quartz	1	6
rhyolite	1	8
rock set	1	7
unknown mineral	1 sample	6
Rock chips	1 package	9

Item	Quantity per Group	Laboratory Investigation
Sand	1 package	12, 13, 14
Sawdust	1 package	4
Screen	1	9
Sieve, small	1	12
Shovel, hand	1	12
Soil samples		
parent material	1	11
subsoil	1	11
topsoil	1	11
Spring scale	1	6
Strainers, fine	2	10
Streak plate	1	5
Stream table	1	13
Teasing needle	1	11
Test-tube holder	1	8
Test tubes, small	3	8
with stopper	1	11
Thread	1	6
Timer	1	9, 14
Tongs	1	8
Tray, white	1	12
Waxed paper	1 roll	1
Wooden block, 4 cm × 10 cm	1	13

Suppliers of Laboratory Materials and Equipment

Accent Science
P.O. Box 1444
Saginaw, MI 48605

Analytical Scientific
11049 Bandera Road
San Antonio, TX 78250

Andor Chemical Corporation
P.O. Box K
Rochester, NY 14623

Ann Arbor Biologicals
6780 Jackson Road
Ann Arbor, MI 48103

Apple Computer, Inc.
20525 Mariani Avenue
Cupertino, CA 95014

Aquarium and Science Supply
Company
P.O. Box 41
Dresher, PA 19025

Arbor Scientific
P.O. Box 2750
924 North Main Street
Ann Arbor, MI 48106

Bausch & Lomb
Scientific Optical Products Division
P.O. Box 450
1400 North Goodman Street
Rochester, NY 14692-0450

California Corporation of
Biochemical Research
3625 Medford Street
Los Angeles, CA 90063

Carolina Biological Supply Company
2700 York Road
Burlington, NC 27215

Central Scientific Company
(CENCO)
11222 Melrose Avenue
Franklin Park, IL 60131

Chem Scientific, Inc.
67 Chapel Street
Newton, MA 02158

College Biological Supply Company
8857 Mount Israel Road
Escondido, CA 92025

Connecticut Valley Biological
Supply Company, Inc.
P.O. Box 326
82 Valley Road
Southampton, MA 01073

Damon/Instructional Systems
Division
80 Wilson Way
Westwood, MA 02090

Delta Biologicals
P.O. Box 26666
Tucson, AZ 85726-6666

Edmund Scientific Company
101 East Gloucester Pike
Barrington, NJ 08007-1380

Fisher Scientific Company
Educational Materials Division
4901 West LeMoyne Street
Chicago, IL 60651

Flinn Scientific, Inc.
P.O. Box 219
131 Flinn Street
Batavia, IL 60510

Forestry Suppliers, Inc.
P.O. Box 8397
205 West Rankin Street
Jackson, MS 39204

Frey Scientific Company
905 Hickory Lane
Mansfield, OH 44905

General Supply Corporation
P.O. Box 9347
Jackson, MS 39206

Grau-Hall Scientific Corporation
6501 Elvas Avenue
Sacramento, CA 95819

H & H Research, Inc.
P.O. Box 5156, Station One
Wilmington, NC 28403

Hach Company
P.O. Box 389
Loveland, CO 80539

Harvard Apparatus Company
Dover, MA 02118

Hubbard Scientific Company
P.O. Box 104
1946 Raymond Drive
Northbrook, IL 60062

Ideal School Supply Company
11000 South Lavergne Avenue
Oak Lawn, IL 60453

Kons Scientific Company, Inc.
P.O. Box 3
Germantown, WI 53022-0003

La Pine Scientific Company
6001 Knox Avenue
Chicago, IL 60018

Lab-Aids, Inc.
249 Trade Zone Drive
Ronkonkoma, NY 11779

Learning Alternatives
P.O. Box 219
Vienna, OH 44473

Learning Spectrum
1390 Westridge Drive
Portola Valley, CA 94025

Learning Things, Inc.
P.O. Box 436
68A Broadway
Arlington, MA 02174

William A. Lemberger Company
2500 Waukau Avenue
Oshkosh, WI 54903

McKilligan Supply Corporation
435 Main Street
Johnson City, NY 13790

Ben Meadows Company
3589 Broad Street
Chamblee, GA 30341

Merrell Scientific Division
Educational Modules,
  Incorporated
1665 Buffalo Road
Rochester, NY 14624

Nasco
901 Janesville Avenue
Fort Atkinson, WI 53538

Nasco West, Inc.
P.O. Box 3837
Modesto, CA 95352

National Teaching Aids, Inc.
1845 Highland Avenue
New Hyde Park, NY 11040

Niles Biological
P.O. Box 191543
Sacramento, CA 95819

Norris Science Labs & Kits
P.O. Box 61281
Las Vegas, NV 89160

Nutritional Biochemicals
  Corporation
26201 Miles Road
Cleveland, OH 44128

Parco Scientific Company
P.O. Box 189
316 Youngstown-Kingsville Road
Vienna, OH 44473

Phipps and Bird, Inc.
P.O. Box 189
Richmond, VA 23261

Prentice-Hall Equipment Division
10 Oriskany Drive
Tonawanda, NY 14150

Redco Science, Inc.
11 Robinson Lane
Oxford, CT 06483

Sargent-Welch Scientific Company
7300 North Linder Avenue
Skokie, IL 60077

Scavengers Scientific Supply
  Company
P.O. Box 211328
Auke Bay, WI 99821

Schoolmasters Science
P.O. Box 1941
745 State Circle
Ann Arbor, MI 48106

Schwarz BioResearch, Inc.
Mountain View Avenue
Orangeburg, NY 10962

Science Kit and Boreal Labs
777 East Park Drive
Tonawanda, NY 14150

The Science Man Company
A Division of TSM Marketing, Inc.
4738 North Harlem Avenue
Harwood Heights, IL 60656

Scientific Glass Apparatus
  Company
737 Broad Street
Bloomfield, NJ 07003

Southern Precision Instrument
  Company
3419 East Commerce Street
San Antonio, TX 78820

Southwestern Biological Supply
  Company
P.O. Box 4084
Dallas, TX 75208

Spectrum Educational Supplies
  Limited
125 Mary Street
Aurora, Ontario, Canada

Swift Instruments, Inc.
P.O. Box 562
San Jose, CA 95106

Triarch, Inc.
P.O. Box 98
Ripon, WI 59471

Turtox, Inc.
P.O. Box 266
Palos Heights, IL 60463-0266

Ward's Natural Science
  Establishment, Inc.
P.O. Box 92912
5100 West Henrietta Road
Rochester, NY 14692-9012

Wildlife Supply Company
301 Cass Street
Saginaw, MI 48602

Wilkens-Anderson Company
4525 West Division Street
Chicago, IL 60651

Laboratory Manual

DYNAMIC EARTH

Prentice Hall
Englewood Cliffs, New Jersey
Needham, Massachusetts

Laboratory Manual

PRENTICE HALL SCIENCE
Dynamic Earth

ISBN 0-13-986472-5

151617–DBH–97

Prentice Hall
A Division of Simon & Schuster
Englewood Cliffs, New Jersey 07632

Contents

Safety Symbols

All the investigations in this *Laboratory Manual* have been designed with safety in mind. If you follow the instructions, you should have a safe and interesting year in the laboratory. Before beginning any investigation, make sure you read the safety rules that follow.

The eight safety symbols below appear next to certain steps in some of the investigations in this *Laboratory Manual*. The symbols alert you to the need for special safety precautions. The description of each symbol below tells you which precautions to take whenever you see the symbol in an investigation.

Glassware Safety

1. Whenever you see this symbol, you will know that you are working with glassware that can easily be broken. Take particular care to handle such glassware safely. And never use broken or chipped glassware.
2. Never heat glassware that is not thoroughly dry. Never pick up any glassware unless you are sure it is not hot. If it is hot, use heat-resistant gloves.
3. Always clean glassware thoroughly before putting it away.

Fire Safety

1. Whenever you see this symbol, you will know that you are working with fire. Never use any source of fire without wearing safety goggles.
2. Never heat anything—particularly chemicals—unless instructed to do so.
3. Never heat anything in a closed container.
4. Never reach across a flame.
5. Always use a clamp, tongs, or heat-resistant gloves to handle hot objects.
6. Always maintain a clean work area, particularly when using a flame.

Heat Safety

Whenever you see this symbol, you will know that you should put on heat-resistant gloves to avoid burning your hands.

Chemical Safety

1. Whenever you see this symbol, you will know that you are working with chemicals that could be hazardous.
2. Never smell any chemical directly from its container. Always use your hand to waft some of the odors from the top of the container toward your nose—and only when instructed to do so.
3. Never mix chemicals unless instructed to do so.
4. Never touch or taste any chemical unless instructed to do so.
5. Keep all lids closed when chemicals are not in use. Dispose of all chemicals as instructed by your teacher.
6. Immediately rinse with water any chemicals, particularly acids, that get on your skin and clothes. Then notify your teacher.

Eye and Face Safety

1. Whenever you see this symbol, you will know that you are performing an experiment in which you must take precautions to protect your eyes and face by wearing safety goggles.
2. When you are heating a test tube or bottle, always point it away from you and others. Chemicals can splash or boil out of a heated test tube.

Sharp Instrument Safety

1. Whenever you see this symbol, you will know that you are working with a sharp instrument.
2. Always use single-edged razors; double-edged razors are too dangerous.
3. Handle any sharp instrument with extreme care. Never cut any material toward you; always cut away from you.
4. Immediately notify your teacher if your skin is cut.

Electrical Safety

1. Whenever you see this symbol, you will know that you are using electricity in the laboratory.
2. Never use long extension cords to plug in any electrical device. Do not plug too many appliances into one socket or you may overload the socket and cause a fire.
3. Never touch an electrical appliance or outlet with wet hands.

Animal Safety

1. Whenever you see this symbol, you will know that you are working with live animals.
2. Do not cause pain, discomfort, or injury to an animal.
3. Follow your teacher's directions when handling animals. Wash your hands thoroughly after handling animals or their cages.

Science Safety Rules

One of the first things a scientist learns is that working in the laboratory can be an exciting experience. But the laboratory can also be quite dangerous if proper safety rules are not followed at all times. To prepare yourself for a safe year in the laboratory, read over the following safety rules. Then read them a second time. Make sure you understand each rule. If you do not, ask your teacher to explain any rules you are unsure of.

Dress Code

1. Many materials in the laboratory can cause eye injury. To protect yourself from possible injury, wear safety goggles whenever you are working with chemicals, burners, or any substance that might get into your eyes. Never wear contact lenses in the laboratory.
2. Wear a laboratory apron or coat whenever you are working with chemicals or heated substances.
3. Tie back long hair to keep it away from any chemicals, burners, and candles, or other laboratory equipment.
4. Remove or tie back any article of clothing or jewelry that can hang down and touch chemicals and flames.

General Safety Rules

5. Read all directions for an experiment several times. Follow the directions exactly as they are written. If you are in doubt about any part of the experiment, ask your teacher for assistance.
6. Never perform activities that are not authorized by your teacher. Obtain permission before ''experimenting'' on your own.
7. Never handle any equipment unless you have specific permission.
8. Take extreme care not to spill any material in the laboratory. If a spill occurs, immediately ask your teacher about the proper cleanup procedure. Never simply pour chemicals or other substances into the sink or trash container.
9. Never eat in the laboratory.
10. Wash your hands before and after each experiment.

First Aid

11. Immediately report all accidents, no matter how minor, to your teacher.
12. Learn what to do in case of specific accidents, such as getting acid in your eyes or on your skin. (Rinse acids from your body with lots of water.)
13. Become aware of the location of the first-aid kit. But your teacher should administer any required first aid due to injury. Or your teacher may send you to the school nurse or call a physician.
14. Know where and how to report an accident or fire. Find out the location of the fire extinguisher, phone, and fire alarm. Keep a list of important phone numbers—such as the fire department and the school nurse—near the phone. Immediately report any fires to your teacher.

Heating and Fire Safety

15. Again, never use a heat source, such as a candle or a burner, without wearing safety goggles.
16. Never heat a chemical you are not instructed to heat. A chemical that is harmless when cool may be dangerous when heated.
17. Maintain a clean work area and keep all materials away from flames.
18. Never reach across a flame.
19. Make sure you know how to light a Bunsen burner. (Your teacher will demonstrate the proper procedure for lighting a burner.) If the flame leaps out of a burner toward you, immediately turn off the gas. Do not touch the burner. It may be hot. And never leave a lighted burner unattended!
20. When heating a test tube or bottle, always point it away from you and others. Chemicals can splash or boil out of a heated test tube.

21. Never heat a liquid in a closed container. The expanding gases produced may blow the container apart, injuring you or others.
22. Before picking up a container that has been heated, first hold the back of your hand near it. If you can feel the heat on the back of your hand, the container may be too hot to handle. Use a clamp or tongs when handling hot containers.

Using Chemicals Safely

23. Never mix chemicals for the "fun of it." You might produce a dangerous, possibly explosive substance.
24. Never touch, taste, or smell a chemical unless you are instructed by your teacher to do so. Many chemicals are poisonous. If you are instructed to note the fumes in an experiment, gently wave your hand over the opening of a container and direct the fumes toward your nose. Do not inhale the fumes directly from the container.
25. Use only those chemicals needed in the activity. Keep all lids closed when a chemical is not being used. Notify your teacher whenever chemicals are spilled.
26. Dispose of all chemicals as instructed by your teacher. To avoid contamination, never return chemicals to their original containers.
27. Be extra careful when working with acids or bases. Pour such chemicals over the sink, not over your workbench.
28. When diluting an acid, pour the acid into water. Never pour water into the acid.
29. Immediately rinse with water any acids that get on your skin or clothing. Then notify your teacher of any acid spill.

Using Glassware Safely

30. Never force glass tubing into a rubber stopper. A turning motion and lubricant will be helpful when inserting glass tubing into rubber stoppers or rubber tubing. Your teacher will demonstrate the proper way to insert glass tubing.
31. Never heat glassware that is not thoroughly dry. Use a wire screen to protect glassware from any flame.
32. Keep in mind that hot glassware will not appear hot. Never pick up glassware without first checking to see if it is hot. See #22.
33. If you are instructed to cut glass tubing, fire-polish the ends immediately to remove sharp edges.
34. Never use broken or chipped glassware. If glassware breaks, notify your teacher and dispose of the glassware in the proper trash container.
35. Never eat or drink from laboratory glassware.
36. Thoroughly clean glassware before putting it away.

Using Sharp Instruments

37. Handle scalpels or razor blades with extreme care. Never cut material toward you; cut away from you.
38. Immediately notify your teacher if you cut your skin when working in the laboratory.

Animal Safety

39. No experiments that cause pain, discomfort, or harm to mammals, birds, reptiles, fish, and amphibians should be done in the classroom or at home.
40. Animals should be handled only if necessary. If an animal is excited or frightened, pregnant, feeding, or with its young, special handling is required.
41. Your teacher will instruct you as to how to handle each animal species that may be brought into the classroom.
42. Clean your hands thoroughly after handling animals or the cage containing animals.

End-of-Experiment Rules

43. After an experiment has been completed, clean up your work area and return all equipment to its proper place.
44. Wash your hands after every experiment.
45. Turn off all candles and burners before leaving the laboratory. Check that the gas line leading to the burner is off as well.

Laboratory Investigation

Movement of the Earth's Crust

1

Examining Faulting and Folding

You may want to refer students to pages J12–J18 in their textbook for a general discussion of folding and faulting.

Time required: 40 minutes

Background Information

Extremely high pressures and temperatures exist deep in the Earth. Because of these high pressures and temperatures, there is stress on the rocks. Sometimes this stress causes the rocks to bend and fold. Sometimes stress causes rocks to break and move. Breaks along which movement occurs are called faults. These folded or faulted rock layers may be exposed at the Earth's surface.

In this investigation you will examine the processes of folding and faulting.

Problem

How can clay models be used to demonstrate several types of folds and faults?

Materials *(per student)*

3 different colors of modeling clay
waxed paper
knife
golf ball

Procedure

1. Knead and flatten each of the pieces of modeling clay into thin layers on a sheet of waxed paper. Place the layers on top of each other. Using the knife, carefully cut the clay into a large rectangle. **CAUTION:** *Be very careful when using a knife.* The clay will represent the original way the rock layers were formed. Draw and label a cross section, or cut-away view, of the layers in the space provided in Observations.

2. Apply pressure with both hands at either end of the layers as shown in Figure 1.

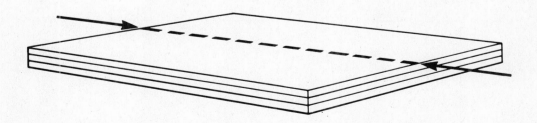

Figure 1

3. Using the knife, carefully cut a cross section through the center of the piece of clay in the same direction that you applied the pressure. See dotted line in Figure 1. Draw the cross section in the space provided in Observations.

4. Take one half of the folded layers and carefully flatten them again. Place the golf ball under the center and push the layers of clay down over it. Remove the ball. Carefully cut through the clay so that you have a cross section of the model of a dome mountain. Draw and label the cross section of the model dome mountain in the space provided in Observations.

5. Take the other half of the folded layers and carefully flatten them too. Then cut across the layers in a direction perpendicular to the original cut. **Note:** *Do not move the clay after you cut it in half.* Now apply pressure with both hands, as shown in Figure 1. You have created a fault. Draw and label a side view of the layers after movement along the fault in the space provided in Observations.

Observations

Cross Section of Unfolded Clay Layers

Cross Section of Folded Layers

Cross Section of Dome Mountain

Cross Section of a Fault

Analysis and Conclusions

1. According to your first drawing, which rock layer would have been formed first? Last? <u>Students should note that the bottom layer would have been formed first, and then the second layer. The top layer would be the youngest, or the layer formed last.</u>

2. Using your second drawing as a reference, answer these questions.
   a. If a syncline were worn away, would you find the oldest rocks at the center or at the edge? Why? <u>At the edge because in a syncline the bottom, or oldest, layer is pushed down in the center and up on either end.</u>

   b. If an anticline were worn away, would you find the oldest rocks at the center or at the edge? Why? <u>At the center because in an anticline the bottom, or oldest, layer is pushed up in the center and down on either end.</u>

3. How can you tell which side of a fault has risen in relation to the other side? <u>By comparing the position of the layers on one side of the fault to the position of the same layers on the other side of the fault.</u>

Critical Thinking and Application

1. How are the processes of mountain and valley formation related to faulting?

As rock layers are forced together, they can buckle upward or downward causing the formation of

mountains and valleys. This can also occur when rock layers are pulled apart.

2. Why must a geologist be careful in trying to determine the ages of rock layers found in a fault or fold? Faulting and folding can cause rock layers to become inverted, thus placing the older

rock layers near the surface and the younger layers at greater depths.

3. When a rubber band is stretched too much, it will break. How does this relate to the rock faulting? Rocks have a limited amount of elasticity. If too much stress is placed on a rock layer, it

will tear or break.

Going Further

Using shoe boxes and crayons, prepare block diagrams of a syncline, anticline, and dome mountain. Color the layers to show the features and then label them. Construct a shoe-box block model of a fault.

Students should draw the features on the outside of the shoe boxes. These block diagrams will provide three-dimensional references for students.

——————————— *Laboratory Investigation* ———————————

Earthquakes and Volcanoes

2

Locating an Epicenter

You may want to refer students to pages J34–J36 in their textbook for a general discussion of earthquake waves.

Time required: 40 minutes

Background Information

Whenever an earthquake occurs, shock waves spread out in all directions. Some of these waves cause rock particles to vibrate from side to side as they pass through the rock. Other types of waves cause rock particles to vibrate forward and backward. Different types of earthquake waves travel through rocky material at different speeds. The earthquake shock waves that travel fastest are known as P, or primary, waves. P waves are also sometimes called push-pull waves. Certain slower waves are referred to as S, or secondary, waves. S waves, also known as shear waves, are the type that cause rock particles to vibrate from side to side. S waves reach locations distant from the earthquake's point of origin somewhat later than P waves. The underground point of origin is called the earthquake's focus. The point on the land surface directly above the focus is known as the epicenter.

To detect earthquake shock waves, geologists use a very sensitive instrument called a seismograph. It can detect even very weak shock waves. From the information recorded by a seismograph, scientists are able to determine the exact arrival times of both P and S waves. Since P waves travel faster than S waves, you have probably realized that you can determine how far away you are from the earthquake's epicenter if you know the difference in the arrival time of the two types of waves. And that is exactly how seismologists determine the distance to an earthquake's epicenter, even when it is thousands of kilometers away. When similar information from stations in different locations is compared, the precise location of the epicenter can be determined.

In this investigation you will duplicate this procedure in a model situation.

Problem

How can an earthquake's epicenter be located?

Materials *(per student)*

drawing compass with pencil   Be sure it has a sharp point!
the accompanying graph
the accompanying map of the
    United States

Procedure

1. Carefully observe Figure 1, which shows a comparison of the difference in arrival time between P and S waves and distance to the epicenter of an earthquake. Note that the two quantities are directly related; that is, the greater the difference in arrival time, the greater the distance to the epicenter.

2. Before going further in this investigation, you will need to become familiar with the graph. Use the graph to answer questions 1 through 4 in Observations.

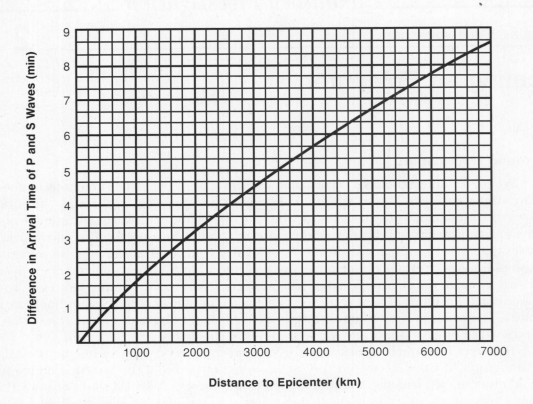

Figure 1

3. Now that you know how to read the graph, see if you can put it to use. Assume that an earthquake has occurred and that the times of arrival of the P and S waves from it have been detected and recorded by seismographs located at the three cities listed in the Data Table. Note that the difference in P and S wave arrival times has been included in the table.

4. Using Figure 1, determine each city's distance from the earthquake epicenter. Enter your figures in the Data Table.

5. Use the map scale to set your compass at a radius equal to the distance from Denver to the earthquake epicenter.

6. Draw a circle with the radius determined in step 5, using Denver as the center. Draw the circle on the map in Figure 2.

7. Repeat steps 5 and 6 for Houston and Miami.

8. If you have worked carefully, the three circles should intersect at one point. This point marks the epicenter of the earthquake.

Observations

DATA TABLE 1

City	Difference in P and S Wave Arrival Time	Distance (km)
Denver, Colorado	2 min 25 sec	1400
Houston, Texas	4 min 10 sec	2700
Miami, Florida	5 min 40 sec	4000

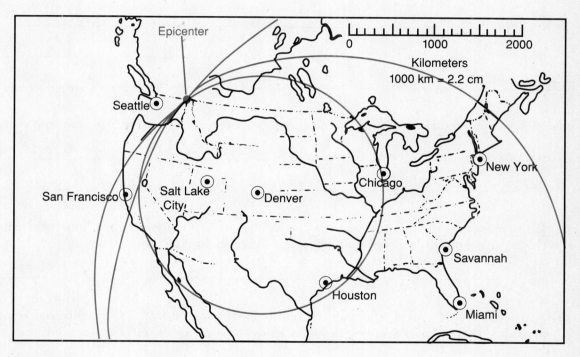

Figure 2

1. If the difference in arrival time for P and S waves at a certain location is 3 min, how far from that station is the epicenter? a. 430 km   b. 1400 km   c. 1800 km   d. 2100 km

2. If a seismograph shows that a P wave arrives 7 min 20 sec before an S wave, how far is it to the earthquake's epicenter? _5600 km_____

3. If a recording station is known to be 4600 km from an earthquake epicenter, what is the difference in arrival time between the P and S waves from that earthquake?

6 min 20 sec

4. If a seismograph is located 2200 km from an earthquake epicenter, how great will be the difference in arrival time between the P and S waves at this station?

3 min 30 sec

Analysis and Conclusions

1. a. Which city on the map is closest to the earthquake epicenter?

Seattle.

b. How far, in km, is this city from the epicenter? About 300 km

2. Which of the three cities listed in the Data Table would have become aware of the earthquake first? Denver.

Second? Houston.

Third? Miami.

3. Why was it necessary to know the distance from the epicenter for at least three recording stations to be able to locate the epicenter? Two recording stations would provide two possible epicenters.

4. If the epicenter of this earthquake were located in San Francisco, how much earlier than the S wave would the P wave arrive for an observer in New York City?

4300 km = 6 min

5. As the distance between an observer and an earthquake decreases, the difference in arrival times of P and S waves a. decreases, b. increases, c. remains the same.

Critical Thinking and Application

1. What can happen to the Earth's surface when the vibrations from an earthquake travel through the crust? An earthquake's vibrations can cause the Earth's crust to shake, fold, or tear.

2. What relationship do you think exists between the amount of energy an earthquake contains and the amount of damage it will do?

Normally, the greater the energy an earthquake contains, the greater the damage it does.

_____

_____

3. Is it possible for seismologists to know for sure that an earthquake or volcanic eruption will not occur in a particular area? Explain your answer.

No, it is not possible. Faults and folds could still be forming in many unmonitored areas. Also, areas of

past activity could be reactivated.

_____

_____

Going Further

Find out about the construction of buildings in earthquake zones. Buildings in areas that have earthquakes are built with certain unique construction features. What do you think some of these features might be? You may want to write to the National Center for Earthquake Research, Geologic Survey Field Center, Menlo Park, CA 94025, and request some information about the construction of earthquake-proof buildings.

Laboratory Investigation

Earthquakes and Volcanoes

3

Investigating the Speed of Earthquake Waves

You may want to refer students to pages J34–J36 in their textbook for a general discussion of earthquake waves.

Time required: 40 minutes

Background Information

When an earthquake occurs, waves are produced that travel outward away from the focus of the earthquake, in much the same way that ripples move across the surface of water when a pebble is thrown into a pond.

Primary waves and secondary waves are two different types of waves produced by an earthquake. They are usually referred to as P waves and S waves. The graphic relationship between how far P and S waves travel and the length of time that they have traveled is an important tool used by scientists who investigate earthquakes.

In this investigation you will construct a P and S wave travel-time graph. You will then use the graph to answer some questions about earthquakes.

Problem

What is an earthquake wave travel-time graph and how is it used?

Materials *(per group)*

pen or pencil

Procedure

1. An earthquake recently occurred producing P and S waves that were recorded by instruments located at the stations identified in the Data Table. The Data Table also indicates the distance traveled and the travel time for each wave. Using the information contained in the Data Table, construct a graph showing the relationship between the distance traveled by P and S waves and their travel time. There will be two slightly curved lines on your graph. Label the curves appropriately as either P wave or S wave.

2. Use the graph that you constructed to answer the questions in Analysis and Conclusions.

Observations

DATA TABLE

Wave Type	Distance Traveled from the epicenter (km)	Travel Time (min)	(sec)
P	1600	3	20
P	6500	9	50
P	5400	8	40
P	2000	4	00
P	9600	12	40
P	700	1	30
P	7000	10	20
P	3400	6	10
P	8800	12	00
P	4000	7	00
S	2200	8	00
S	4000	12	40
S	5200	15	20
S	1700	6	30
S	6000	17	00
S	1100	4	20
S	7400	19	40
S	8200	21	00
S	500	2	10
S	9000	22	10

Analysis and Conclusions

1. a. If an earthquake occurred near where you live, would P waves or S waves arrive at your location first? P waves would arrive first.

   b. Explain your answer. P waves travel faster than S waves.

2. a. How long would it take for a P wave to travel from an earthquake epicenter to a location 8000 km away? Approximately 11 minutes and 20 seconds.

   b. How long would it take for an S wave to travel the same distance?

   Approximately 20 minutes and 40 seconds.

3. Approximately how far must an observer be from an earthquake epicenter if he or she received a P wave 8 minutes after it was produced by the earthquake?

   Approximately 4800 km.

4. Explain how you could tell which of two observers was farthest from an earthquake epicenter by comparing the arrival times of P and S waves for the two locations.

   P waves travel faster than S waves; the longer they travel, the farther apart they become. Therefore, the

   observer that noted the greatest difference in arrival times for the P and S waves must have been

   farthest from the epicenter.

Earthquake S Wave and P Wave Travel-Time Graph

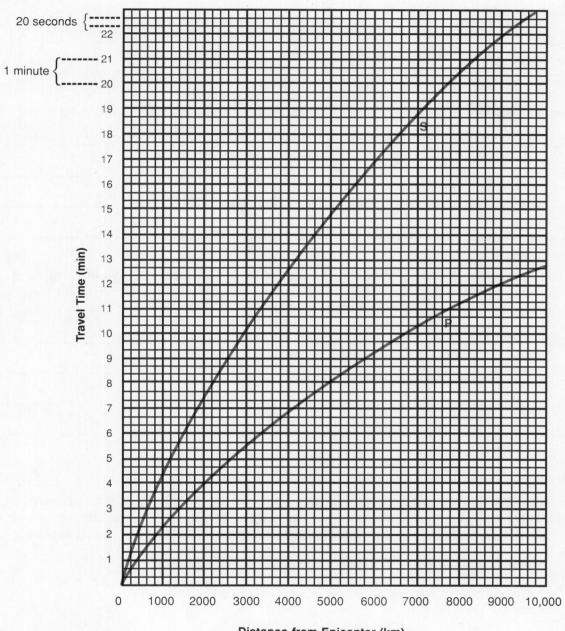

20 seconds

1 minute

Distance from Epicenter (km)

Note: *Be certain that the students are aware that the vertical axis is divided into 20-second intervals.*

Critical Thinking and Application

1. How far from an earthquake epicenter would an observer be if he or she measured a difference of 8 minutes and 40 seconds in the arrival times of a P and S wave?

   7000 km.

2. What kinds of landforms would you be most likely to find in an earthquake zone?

   Answers will vary but may include mountains, valleys, faults, folds, domes, and volcanoes.

3. A tsunami is a large sea wave started by an earthquake. Why is a tsunami so dangerous?

   Since the vibrations come from under the water, the entire depth of the water is affected. This rapidly

   moving wall of water can wipe out entire communities, causing tremendous loss of life and property.

4. States along the west coast of the United States, such as California and Washington, have experienced much earthquake and volcanic activity. What does this indicate about the underlying rock structure of this part of the country?

   The rock layers under the surface are under extreme pressure. The resulting stress has caused the

   layers to fault.

Going Further

Use reference books to find the locations and dates of earthquakes that have occurred in the United States. Using a map, plot the location of these earthquakes. Do there seem to be areas in the United States where earthquakes are more common? How would you explain this?

Laboratory Investigation

4

Observing Convection Currents

You may want to refer students to pages J67–J71 in their textbook for a general discussion of convection currents and plate movement.

Time required: 35 minutes

Background Information

Many scientists think that there are convection currents of hot rock within the mantle of the Earth. They think that the hot rock rises and flows out along the ridges. As this process goes on along the ridges, new ocean floor is created that pushes older ocean floor toward the continents. These scientists think that the continents are gradually moving because of these convection currents.

In this investigation you will construct a working model of a convection current and study its action.

Problem

How can a model of a convection current be prepared and used to illustrate ocean-floor spreading?

Materials *(per group)*

400-mL beaker   food coloring
Bunsen burner or candle   sawdust
ring stand   beaker clamp

Procedure

🔺 **1.** Fill the beaker about three-fourths full with water.

🔺 **2.** Place the beaker into the beaker clamp and attach the clamp to the ring stand. See Figure 1.

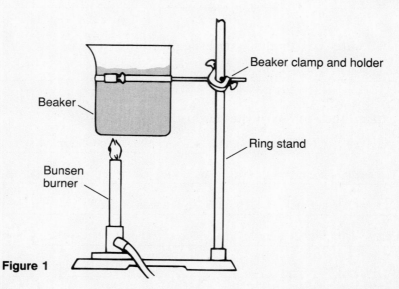

Figure 1

🔥 **3.** Light and adjust the flame on the burner you are using.

⚗️🔥 **4.** Adjust the beaker on the ring stand so that the flame of the burner is directly heating only one side of the beaker.

⚗️🔥 **5.** When the water just begins to boil, add a few drops of food coloring. Draw arrows in Figure 2 to show the path of the food coloring.

⚗️🔥 **6.** Turn off the burner and allow the water in the beaker to cool a little. Carefully sprinkle a fine layer of sawdust over the surface of the water.

⚗️🔥 **7.** Relight your burner and adjust the flame. Heat one side of the beaker as you did in step 4.

8. Observe what happens to the sawdust as you look from above.

9. Turn off your burner. Allow your apparatus to cool completely before dismantling it.

Observations

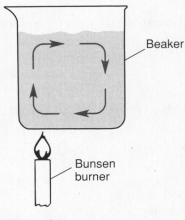

Figure 2

Analysis and Conclusions

1. Explain the pattern formed by the food coloring.

The heated water was less dense so it rose and traveled along the top until it cooled, and sank, only to

be heated once again.

2. Where was "new" water constantly being brought to the surface?

Above the heat source.

3. Describe and explain the motion of the sawdust.

The sawdust moved from one side where the heat was and piled up on the other side. Convection

currents carried the sawdust from one side to the other. As the heated water cooled, it sank. The

sawdust did not sink with it, but instead piled up along the side of the beaker, in much the same way

rock heated in the mantle moves up to the surface, cools, and piles up against the continents or is

pushed down into the mantle.

Critical Thinking and Application

1. How does the model you prepared compare to convection currents in the Earth's interior?

   Rock is heated and moves up to the surface, where it cools and sometimes piles up against the

   continents or is pushed down into the mantle.

   _____

   _____

2. If two moving continents collided as a result of the convection currents that occurred beneath them, what changes might occur on the surface of the continents?

   As the two continents collided, they might buckle upward and form mountains.

   _____

   _____

3. Why is it important for scientists to know where plate boundaries are located?

   By knowing the locations of plate boundaries, scientists can identify areas of stress and pressure that

   will be more likely to experience volcanic and earthquake activity.

   _____

Going Further

Make a large diagram of how a convection current might work deep under the ocean floor. Use posterboard, crayons, colored pencils, and paint.

Laboratory Investigation

5

Identifying Common Minerals

You may want to refer students to pages J80–J87 in their textbook for a general discussion of minerals.

Time required: 40 minutes

Background Information

Scientists have identified more than 2000 different kinds of minerals. However, most minerals are very rare. Over 95 percent of the Earth's crust is made of rocks that are composed of about a dozen minerals. These common minerals are called rock-forming minerals. While minerals can vary a great deal in their chemical makeup and the forms in which they are found, most common minerals can be identified by observing a few of their basic properties.

In this investigation you will observe the physical properties of some common rock-forming minerals and use these properties to identify the minerals. To do so, you will have to test for the physical properties described below.

SOME PHYSICAL PROPERTIES OF MINERALS

Hardness is the resistance of a mineral to scratching. A mineral will scratch any other substance less hard than itself.

Table of Hardness of Common Items	
Item	**Approximate Hardness**
Fingernail	2.5
Copper penny	3.0
Steel nail	5.5
Glass	6.0

This means a fingernail will scratch the mineral.

In this case, see if the mineral will scratch the glass to avoid students breaking the glass in their hands.

Streak is the color of a fine powder of a mineral. Rubbing a mineral against a piece of dull tile, or streak plate, will powder enough of the mineral to enable you to determine its streak.

Cleavage is the quality of a mineral that causes it to split, leaving smooth, flat surfaces. When a mineral does not split to leave smooth, flat surfaces, the break is called a fracture. You can easily observe whether a mineral shows cleavage or fracture.

Minerals have a characteristic *crystal shape*. A crystal is a solid that has flat surfaces, or faces, arranged in a definite shape. There are six crystal systems, or categories of crystal shapes: cubic, hexagonal, orthorhombic, monoclinic, tetragonal, and triclinic. Most minerals belong to only one crystal system. A few, however, belong to more than one system. Serpentine crystals, for example, may be monoclinic, orthorhombic, or hexagonal. Although the crystals in each system share certain basic mathematical characteristics, they may appear quite different from one another. Consider three minerals whose crystals belong to the cubic system: halite, diamond, and garnet. Halite crystals, which are shaped like tiny cubes, have six square faces. Diamond crystals have eight triangular faces. And garnet crystals have twelve faces, each of which has five sides.

Luster is the way a mineral reflects light. Minerals may be described as having metallic or nonmetallic luster. Metallic luster is the shine associated with a freshly polished metal surface. Nonmetallic luster may be described by terms such as glassy, brilliant, or greasy.

Density is the mass, per unit volume of a substance. Density can be estimated by determining a sample's heft, or how heavy it seems for its size. Samples that seem heavy for their size are described as dense, while samples that seem light for their size are described as not very dense.

Some minerals have *special properties* that can be used to identify them. For example, a few minerals are magnetic and will be attracted to a magnet.

Problem

How can the physical properties of minerals be used to identify them?

Materials *(per group)*

set of common mineral samples
magnet
piece of dull tile (streak plate)
hardness kit containing a
    copper penny, a steel nail, and
    a piece of glass (scratch plate)

Paint small spots or add tape to each mineral sample. Then number each mineral. Retain a key of your number code for easy reference to mineral type.

Available from all science supply companies.

Procedure

Carefully test and observe each mineral sample to determine its physical characteristics. Use the summary of mineral physical properties in the Mineral Identification Key on the next page. Enter your observations in the appropriate space in the Data Table.

Mineral Identification Key

Directions: Determine the identity of your samples by comparing their properties with the descriptions listed in the key. Start at the left and work to the right while progressively narrowing the possibilities.

Metallic luster

Black, green-black or dark green streak

Black; strongly magnetic; hardness, 6	Magnetite
Lead-pencil black; smudges fingers; hardness, 1 to 2	Graphite
Brass yellow; cubic crystals; hardness, 6 to 6.5	Pyrite
Brass yellow, may be tarnished purple; hardness, 3.5 to 4	Chalcopyrite
Shiny gray; very heavy; cubic cleavage; hardness, 2.5	Galena

Brown or white streak

Yellow-brown to dark brown, may be almost black; hardness, 5 to 5.5	Limonite
Yellow-brown; streak white to pale yellow; resinous luster; hardness, 3.5 to 4	Sphalerite
Red to brown streak; hardness 5.5 to 6.5	Hematite

Nonmetallic, light-colored

Scratches glass

Cleavage

Pink to bluish gray to green; 2 cleavage planes at right angles; hardness, 6	Orthoclase

No cleavage

Glassy luster; crystals are 6-sided when present; hardness, 7; shell-like fracture	Quartz
Glassy luster; shades of green and yellow; hardness, 6.5 to 7	Olivine

Does not scratch glass

Cleavage

Colorless to white; salty taste; cubic cleavage; hardness, 2.5	Halite
White or yellow to colorless; hardness, 3; double image seen when crystal is placed on printed page	Calcite
White to transparent; hardness, 2	Gypsum
Green to white; feels soapy; hardness, 1	Talc
Colorless to light yellow; hardness, 2 to 2.5; cleavage in flat sheets	Muscovite
White, yellow, purple, or green; 8-sided cleavage; hardness, 4	Fluorite

Nonmetallic, dark-colored

Scratches glass

Cleavage

Black; cleavage with 2 planes at 90° angles; hardness, 5 to 6	Augite
Black; cleavage with 2 planes at 60° angles; hardness, 5 to 6	Hornblende

No cleavage

Gray, brown, blue-gray, pink, white, red; 6-sided crystals; hardness, 9	Corundum
Reddish brown; fracture resembles poor cleavage; brittle; hardness 6.5 to 7.5	Garnet

Does not scratch glass

Cleavage

Brown to black; hardness 2.5 to 3	Biotite
Shades of green; hardness, 2 to 2.5	Chlorite

No cleavage

Green, brown, blue, or purple; shell-like fracture; hardness, 5	Apatite

Observations

DATA TABLE

Mineral Number	Color	Streak Color	Luster (Check One)		The Mineral Shows: (Check One)		Hardness (Check One)			Other Observed Properties	Mineral Name
			Metallic	Nonmetallic	Cleavage	Fracture	Less Than 2.5	2.5–6.0	More Than 6.0		

Analysis and Conclusions

Using the Mineral Identification Key and your observations in the Data Table, identify each mineral and enter its name in the Data Table.

Critical Thinking and Application

1. According to the Mineral Identification Key, what is the only physical property that can be used to distinguish between pyrite and chalcopyrite, assuming that both minerals are the same color?

Hardness.

2. What are the two softest minerals listed in the Mineral Identification Key?

Graphite and talc.

3. What is the hardest mineral listed in the Mineral Identification Key? What must then be true about this mineral? Corundum. This mineral must be able to scratch all other minerals listed in the Key.

4. Which physical property is the least helpful in identifying minerals? The most helpful?

Color of mineral. Special property, if any, streak, cleavage.

5. Explain the following statement: You can determine the identity of a mineral by showing what it *cannot* be. Classification is a process of elimination. By showing what a mineral is not, you can determine what it is.

Going Further

Collect mineral samples from around your school or home. Perform the mineral characteristics tests on your samples. Then see if you can identify each sample. A mineral identification guide might be useful in identifying unknown samples.

Laboratory Investigation

Rocks and Minerals

6

Calculating the Specific Gravity of Minerals

You may want to refer students to pages J80–J87 in their textbook for a general discussion of minerals.

Time required: 40 minutes

Background Information

One of the most important properties of a mineral is specific gravity. Specific gravity is the ratio of the mass of a substance to the mass of an equal volume of water. Specific gravity is an important property of a substance because it is always the same regardless of the size of the sample tested. Therefore, specific gravity can be very useful when trying to identify minerals.

Archimedes, a Greek scientist, discovered that when an object is submerged in water, the mass of the water displaced by the object is equal to the apparent loss of mass of the object in the water. This principle can be used to determine specific gravity.

In this investigation you will learn a way to determine specific gravity and you will use it to determine the specific gravity of three minerals. Then you will use your data to identify an unknown mineral.

Problem

How can you determine specific gravity? How can you use specific gravity to identify minerals?

Materials (*per group*)

thread
spring scale (grams)
ring stand
burette clamp
250-mL beaker
pyrite, quartz, and galena
    samples
unknown sample

Coat the unknown mineral samples with colored nail polish or paint a day before beginning this investigation.

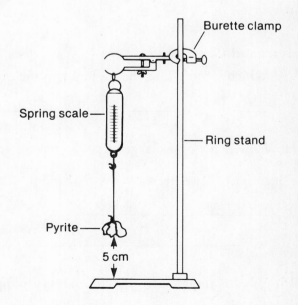

Figure 1

Procedure

1. Tie a length of thread firmly to the sample of pyrite. Attach the other end of the thread to the spring scale. Suspend the spring scale from the burette clamp so that the pyrite is about 5 cm from the table. See Figure 1. Record the mass of the sample in the Data Table.

2. Fill the beaker three-quarters full with water. Place the beaker of water under the spring scale so that the pyrite is completely covered by the water but not touching the sides or the bottom of the beaker. Record the apparent mass in water in the Data Table.

3. Calculate the apparent loss of mass by subtracting the apparent mass in water from the mass in air. Record your answer in the Data Table.

4. The apparent loss of mass of pyrite you just calculated is equal to the mass of water displaced. Record this in the Data Table.

5. Calculate the specific gravity of pyrite. Record your answer in the Data Table.

$$\text{Specific gravity} = \frac{\text{mass of the mineral in air}}{\text{mass of water displaced by the mineral}}$$

6. Repeat steps 1 through 5 for quartz and galena. Record your answers in the Data Table.

7. Obtain an unknown mineral sample from your teacher. It has been covered with paint to disguise the color. Find the specific gravity and record it in the Data Table.
Note: *The paint may change the specific gravity slightly but not enough to affect the experiment.*

Observations

DATA TABLE	Pyrite	Quartz	Galena	Unknown Sample
Mass in air				
Apparent mass in water		Answers will vary.		
Apparent loss of mass in water				
Mass of water displaced				
Specific gravity	5.0–5.1	2.6	7.5	

Analysis and Conclusions

1. Which mineral has the highest specific gravity? The lowest?

   Galena. Quartz.

2. How many times larger than a piece of galena would a piece of quartz have to be in order to have the same mass? Explain. About three times larger because quartz has a specific gravity about one-third the specific gravity of galena.

3. What is the identity of the unknown sample? How can you tell?

   Answers will vary. Its specific gravity is the same as one of the three minerals investigated.

Critical Thinking and Application

1. Why would you not use specific gravity alone to identify minerals?

Two minerals could have specific gravities that were close. Specific gravity should be used in combination

with other properties such as hardness, streak, and so forth.

_____

2. Pyrite is sometimes called "fool's gold" because its color and appearance are similar to real gold. How could a scientist determine if a sample was real gold?

A scientist could determine the specific gravity. Note: *Specific gravity of fool's gold is 5, pure gold 19.*

_____

3. How could a jeweler determine if a sample was pure gold mixed with some other metal?

The jeweler could determine the specific gravity and compare it to the known specific gravity of pure

gold, 19.

_____

4. Explain how specific gravity and density are related.

Specific gravity is the ratio of the mass of a substance to the mass of an equal volume of water. Mass

per unit volume is equal to density. So specific gravity is actually the density of a substance compared to

the density of water.

_____

_____

5. Based on your answer to question 4, explain why specific gravity is a number with no units. The ratio, or comparison, is density of substance divided by density of water. The units of density

(g/mL or g/cm^3) cancel upon division.

_____

_____

_____

Going Further

Try to determine the specific gravity of a substance that floats and a substance that dissolves in water. Devise a way to determine the specific gravity of a piece of ice or a cork. Devise a way to determine the specific gravity of rock candy or halite.

Laboratory Investigation

7

Classifying Rocks

You may want to refer students to pages J93–J97 in their textbook for a general discussion of rock classification.

Time required: 40 minutes

Background Information

The Earth's crust is made of rocks. Scientists place all rocks in categories called classes according to the way the rocks were formed. The three major classes of rocks are sedimentary rocks, igneous rocks, and metamorphic rocks. Rocks from each class tend to show characteristics that are the result of the conditions that existed at the time they were formed. Using these characteristics, almost any rock sample can be identified as belonging to one of the three classes.

In this investigation you will examine several rock samples. Then, given a list of some of the major characteristics of the three classes, you will place each rock sample in the proper class. Below you will find lists of some of the more common characteristics of each class of rock.

Characteristics of Sedimentary Rocks
Examples: sandstone, conglomerate, shale, soft coal

1. Most sedimentary rocks are composed of fragments of other rocks that look very much like sediment. Some sedimentary rocks have a range of particle sizes, while other sedimentary rocks consist mainly of one sediment size. See Figure 1.

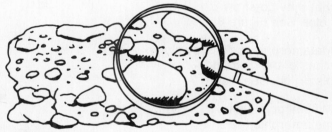

Figure 1

2. Some sedimentary rocks are of organic origin; that is, they are composed of plant and animal products or remains. Such rocks often contain fossils. See Figure 2.

3. Sedimentary rocks often have distinct parallel layers. See Figure 3.

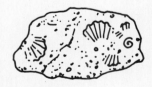

Figure 2

4. Sedimentary rocks often appear dull or earthy.

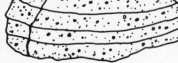

Figure 3

Characteristics of Igneous Rocks

Examples: granite, basalt, obsidian, pumice, gabbro

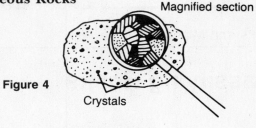

Figure 4

Crystals

Magnified section

1. Igneous rocks may contain crystals, which frequently can be seen by the unaided eye. See Figure 4.

2. Some igneous rocks (those that cooled rapidly) contain no crystals and therefore appear glassy. See Figure 5.

3. Igneous rocks may be found in many colors and often show different-colored crystals that are not in bands.

Figure 5

Characteristics of Metamorphic Rocks

Examples: schist, gneiss, quartzite, slate, marble, hard coal

1. Metamorphic rocks often may look like igneous rocks except that they do show bands of color. See Figure 6.

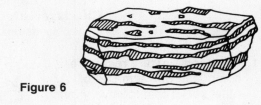

Figure 6

2. Metamorphic rocks may show signs of bending and distortion. See Figure 7.

3. Mineral crystals in metamorphic rocks will generally be flattened.

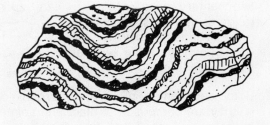

Figure 7

Problem

How can rock samples be identified according to rock class?

Materials (*per group*)

set of natural rock samples
magnifying glass

Select and number samples that clearly exemplify characteristics of each rock class.

Procedure

1. Select one of the numbered rock samples provided by your teacher and examine it carefully.   Rock samples should be identified by first painting a white patch on the sample and then numbering the sample with a marking pencil.

2. After you have determined the sample's most obvious physical properties, compare them to the lists of major characteristics for each of the three classes of rock.

3. Select the rock class that contains descriptions of rocks having properties that best fit the characteristics of the sample you have just observed.
Remind students not to "jump to conclusions" and to check the descriptions of each rock class.

4. Place a check in the box in the Data Table that properly identifies the class your rock sample seems to fit. In the space provided, list the characteristics possessed by your sample that guided you toward your decision. Notice that information describing rock sample A has been completed for you. This will serve as a model or aid toward proper completion of this investigation.   The rock described in Example A is granite.

5. Repeat the above procedure for each of the samples provided.

Observations

Complete the Data Table on page 38.

Analysis and Conclusions

1. List three physical properties that help to identify a given rock sample as a sedimentary rock.   See characteristics list. _____

   _____

   _____

2. List three physical properties that help to identify a given rock sample as an igneous rock.
See characteristics list. _____

   _____

   _____

3. List three physical properties that help to identify a given rock sample as a metamorphic rock.   See characteristics list. _____

   _____

   _____

DATA TABLE Answers will vary depending on specific rock samples. About 12 samples are needed for a 45-minute class period.

	Rock Class			Description
Sample A	Sed.	Ig.	Meta.	*This rock has lots of little sparkling particles that look like crystals. There are four different colors of crystals and they are not bands of color.*
		✓		
Sample 1	Sed.	Ig.	Meta.	
Sample 2	Sed.	Ig.	Meta.	
Sample 3	Sed.	Ig.	Meta.	
Sample 4	Sed.	Ig.	Meta.	
Sample 5	Sed.	Ig.	Meta.	
Sample 6	Sed.	Ig.	Meta.	
Sample 7	Sed.	Ig.	Meta.	
Sample 8	Sed.	Ig.	Meta.	
Sample 9	Sed.	Ig.	Meta.	
Sample 10	Sed.	Ig.	Meta.	
Sample 11	Sed.	Ig.	Meta.	
Sample 12	Sed.	Ig.	Meta.	

Critical Thinking and Application

1. A fossil is the remains or evidence of a living thing. Explain why fossils are rarely found in igneous or metamorphic rocks. The intense heat and pressure that act upon metamorphic and igneous rocks would probably destroy fossils.

_____

_____

_____

2. Why might metamorphic rocks show signs of bending and distortion?

Metamorphic rocks form when other types of rocks are subjected to great heat and pressure. The distortion would result from the pressure acting on the rock.

_____

_____

3. Why might metamorphic rocks be more likely to show bands of color than igneous rocks?

Since other types of rocks are changed into metamorphic rocks, and since this process may go on for a considerable length of time, several bands of color may result. Igneous rocks are more likely to be monochromatic because they are formed when one type of molten rock cools and hardens.

_____

_____

Going Further

Collect various kinds of rocks from your neighborhood. Use the descriptions given in this investigation to classify as many different samples as you can.

Laboratory Investigation

8

Relating Cooling Rate and Crystal Size

You may want to refer students to pages J98–J99 in their textbook for a general discussion of cooling rate and crystal sizes.

Time required: 40 minutes

Background Information

All rocks are made up of one or more minerals. Some rocks are formed from molten rock. When molten rock cools and hardens, it forms igneous rocks. Igneous rocks may contain crystals. The size of the crystals depends upon how quickly the molten rock that forms the igneous rocks cools. Some igneous rocks do not have crystals, while others may have small or large crystals.

In this investigation you will form crystals from melted material. You will observe how the cooling rate affects the size of the crystals that are formed.

Problem

How does cooling rate affect the size of crystals?

Materials *(per group)*

3 glass caster cups
3 small test tubes
test-tube holder
paradichlorobenzene (PDB) flakes   PDB flakes can be obtained in supermarkets, hardware stores, and
hot plate   pharmacies.
magnifying glass
glass-marking pencil
crushed ice
500-mL beaker
400-mL beaker
150-mL beaker
tongs
paper towels
rock samples of rhyolite, granite,
    and obsidian

Procedure   CAUTION: *The room should be well ventilated during this investigation.*

1. Fill the 400-mL beaker three-quarters full with water. Place a caster cup in the beaker. Boil the water on the hot plate. **CAUTION:** *Observe safety procedures when using a hot plate.*

2. Fill the 500-mL beaker with crushed ice. Place the second caster cup in the beaker. Leave the third caster cup at room temperature.

3. Fill each of the three small test tubes with paradichlorobenzene (PDB) flakes.

4. Half fill the 150-mL beaker with water. Place the three test tubes in the beaker. Place the beaker with the test tubes on the hot plate. **CAUTION:** *Work in a well-ventilated room.* Heat the beaker gently until the paradichlorobenzene melts.

5. Using the tongs, carefully remove the caster cup from the boiling water. Have your partner quickly dry the cup. Using the test-tube holder, remove one test tube from the beaker. Pour the PDB in this test tube into the caster cup. Time how long it takes for the PDB to completely become a solid. Label the caster cup A and record the time in the Data Table.

6. Remove the second caster cup from the beaker with ice and dry it quickly and completely. Using the test-tube holder, pour the second test tube of PDB into this cup. Time how long it takes for the PDB to completely turn solid. Label this cup B and record the time in the Data Table.

7. Using the test-tube holder, pour the third test tube of PDB into the caster cup at room temperature. Again, time how long it takes for this PDB to completely turn solid. Label this caster cup C and record the time in the Data Table.

8. Look at the contents of each caster cup with the magnifying glass. Draw the contents of each caster cup in the spaces provided in Observations.

9. Look at the crystals in the samples of rhyolite, granite, and obsidian with a magnifying glass. Draw the crystals in each sample in the spaces provided in Observations.

Observations

DATA TABLE

Caster Cup	Time
A	
B	
C	

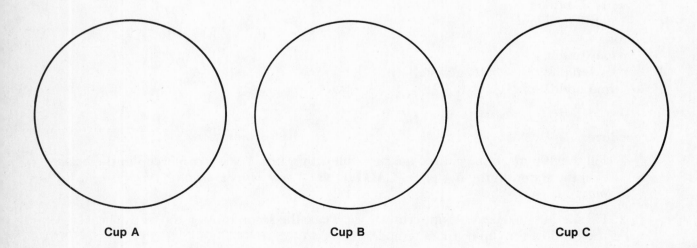

Cup A   Cup B   Cup C

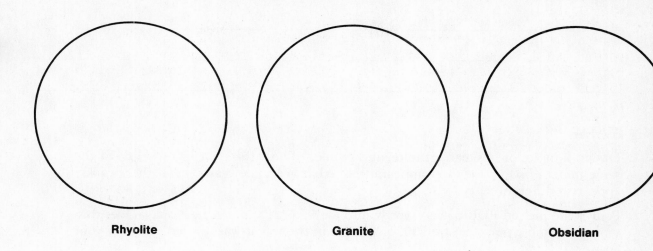

| Rhyolite | Granite | Obsidian |

Analysis and Conclusions

1. Compare the crystals in the caster cups to the samples of granite, rhyolite, and obsidian. Which PDB crystals are most similar to the crystals in the rock samples?

   Cup A: granite   Cup B: obsidian   Cup C: rhyolite

2. How does the rate of cooling affect the size of crystals?

   The slower a melt cools, the larger the crystals.

3. Granite, rhyolite, and obsidian are essentially made of the same materials. Explain why they look different.

   Granite cooled slowly and crystals were able to form. Rhyolite cooled more rapidly than granite, but more

   slowly than obsidian.

Critical Thinking and Application

1. Where would igneous rocks have a chance to cool slowly?

   Deep in the Earth.

2. Where would igneous rocks cool rapidly?

   On the surface of the Earth.

3. In general, if you saw a rock that contained large, interlocking crystals, what would you conclude about the way it formed?

It formed slowly from a melt, probably deep inside the Earth.

Going Further

1. Obtain samples of obsidian, granite, and pumice. These three rocks are made of the same minerals. Describe their appearances. What are some reasons that these rocks appear so different?

2. Pour some melted PDB flakes directly into ice water. Examine the results. Does this mostly resemble pumice, obsidian, or granite in the way it was formed? Explain your answer.

_____ *Laboratory Investigation* _____

9

Investigating Rock Abrasion

You may want to refer students to pages J114–J119 in their textbook for a general discussion of weathering.

Time required: 40 minutes

Background Information

Substances on the Earth are constantly undergoing change. One type of change occurs when rocks are broken into smaller pieces and then rounded as they are moved about in rivers and streams. This kind of change is known as a physical change. The process of rubbing and bumping together that causes this kind of physical change is called abrasion.

In this investigation you will observe the physical changes that rocks undergo through the process of abrasion in a model situation.

Problem

What effect does length of time of abrasion have on the way rock particles weather?

Materials *(per group)*

bottle, jar, or can with lid   Plastic refrigerator jars with wide mouths work well.
presoaked rock chips   Rock should be shale, marble, or gypsum. Marble chips from a local gardening
triple-beam balance   store would work well.
screen   Use pieces of window screen cut to size.
clock or timer

Procedure

1. Obtain a sample of presoaked rock chips and drain them to remove excess water. **Note:** *Place the rocks on the screen so that they do not get lost.* The sample students select could be a couple of handfuls in a paper towel. Soak the chips overnight. Have students pat off excess water with paper towels.

2. Use the balance to measure out 100 g of rock from your sample. Return the extra pieces to the supply container.

3. Place the 100 g of chips in the container provided.

4. Add water to the container until it is about half full. Close the lid tightly over the container. Shake the container at a constant rate for 3 minutes.   You can use taped music to provide a regular beat.

5. Carefully pour the water from the container into a sink. Use the screen to make sure not even the smallest rock piece is lost.

6. Measure the mass of the chips again and record your result in the Data Table.

7. Return the rock chips to the container, close the container, and repeat steps 4 through 6 four more times. Record the results after each 3 minutes of shaking, for a total of 15 minutes.

8. Graph the results, comparing mass remaining with time of shaking.

Observations

Weathering Time (min)	Mass of Rock Remaining (g)
0	100
3	
6	Answers will vary.
9	
12	
15	

GRAPH

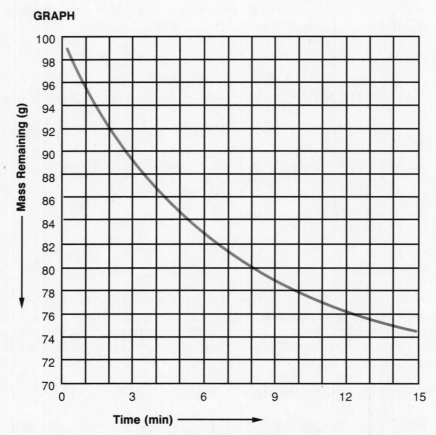

Actual results will vary, but the general trend will show more rapid loss in the first few seconds.

Analysis and Conclusions

1. Why were the rock chips presoaked before you used them? To account for the mass of water that would be picked up during the first shaking period.

2. As you examined the rock pieces after each shaking period, how did the amount of rounding change as the abrasion time increased? Chips lost roughest edges first, then other less rough edges next, becoming more round through time.

3. From your data in the Data Table, describe how the mass remaining changed through time. It decreased, at first rapidly, then slowly.

4. Did the difference in mass remaining at the end of each shaking period change in a regular manner? No.

Explain why you think the mass remaining changed in the way that it did. The most mass was lost during the first and second period because that was when the rough edges were worn off.

5. What do you think might happen to the rate (speed) at which the rock chips were being worn away if you continued to shake them for an hour?
It would decrease, even though the chips would continue to abrade.

6. What effect do you think the shape of the rock chips had on the rate of abrasion?
The rougher the rock the faster the rate. The smoother and rounder the rock the slower the rate.

Critical Thinking and Application

1. How do you think the hardness of a rock would affect the rate at which it would weather? Soft rocks will weather more rapidly than hard rocks.

2. Do you think the rate at which water moves over a rock affects how rapidly the rock weathers? Explain your answer. Yes. A rock weathers more rapidly by fast-moving water than by slow-moving water.

3. The pyramids that were built thousands of years ago in the deserts of Egypt have experienced some weathering due to abrasion. What do you think is responsible for this

abrasion? Sand found in the deserts of Egypt causes weathering as it blows past the pyramids. The

abrasive texture of the sand slowly wears down the surfaces of the rocks.

Going Further

Repeat the procedure with rock salt (halite) chips of the same size. Describe any differences in the rate of abrasion that you observed between the halite and the rock chips that you used the first time. Explain why you think the rock salt weathered in the way that it did.

_____ *Laboratory Investigation* _____

10

Observing the Effects of Chemical Weathering on Chalk

You may want to refer students to pages J114–J119 in their textbook for a general discussion of weathering.

Time required: 30 minutes

Background Information

Rocks are gradually broken apart into smaller and smaller pieces by weathering. Weathering is caused by wind, water, or other natural forces. Sometimes weathering is caused by chemical reactions. One important factor that affects the rate of chemical weathering is the size of the particles.

In this investigation you will observe the relationship between particle size and reaction rate. This investigation will also help you understand how a form of chemical weathering works in nature.

Problem

How does the size of particles affect the rate of chemical weathering?

Materials *(per group)*

2 250-mL beakers
100 mL of dilute hydrochloric
   acid
2 pieces of classroom chalk
triple-beam balance
2 fine food strainers
paper towels

Procedure

1. Carefully pour 100 mL of dilute hydrochloric acid into each beaker. **CAUTION:** *Be careful not to spill acid on your clothing or skin. If you accidentally spill any acid on your clothing or skin, wash immediately with water.*

2. Using the triple-beam balance, find the mass of each piece of chalk. Record the masses in the Data Table. They should be about the same.

3. Break one piece of chalk into several small pieces.

4. Simultaneously place the broken chalk and the unbroken chalk into the two beakers of acid. Observe what happens.

5. Wait a few minutes. Pour the contents of one beaker through one strainer. Pour the contents of the other beaker through the second strainer. Allow the acid to go into the sink. Gently run the water for a minute or two.

6. Gently dry both samples of chalk with paper towels.

7. Find the mass of each sample of chalk. Record the masses in the Data Table. Calculate the amount of chalk that reacted in each beaker and complete the Data Table.

Observations

DATA TABLE

Setup	Masses	
	Whole Piece of Chalk	**Broken Pieces**
Mass before being placed in acid		
Mass after being placed in acid	Answers will vary.	
Amount of chalk that reacted with the acid		

Analysis and Conclusions

1. In which beaker did the reaction proceed more rapidly?

The beaker with the broken chalk.

2. Besides the difference in mass, how else could you tell that one reaction was faster than the other? The rate of bubbling was faster in the beaker with the smaller pieces of chalk.

3. In which beaker was more surface area of chalk exposed to the acid?

The beaker with the broken pieces.

4. In nature, which would weather more rapidly—a 10-kg piece of limestone or 10 1-kg pieces? Why? Ten 1-kg pieces because they have more surface area.

Critical Thinking and Application

1. In order to burn fuel oil more efficiently, some companies are selling a device that sprays the oil into the burner in a fine mist. Do you think this is a good idea? Explain your

   answer. Yes. By spraying the oil into the burner in a fine mist, more surface area will be exposed and

   more of the oil will be burned.

   _____

   _____

2. If flour is in a bag, it is very hard to ignite. However, bakeries will not permit flames in rooms where flour dust may be in the air. They fear an explosion. Why should they be so

   careful? The surface area of the flour particles will be greater, therefore they will be much more likely to

   chemically react and explode.

   _____

   _____

3. How might a layer of topsoil protect a rock layer from chemical weathering?

   The soil could prevent moisture, acids and other chemicals, and gases from touching and reacting with

   the rock layer.

   _____

   _____

4. Why might chemical weathering occur more rapidly in a highly populated city?

   Areas of greater population tend to be more highly polluted. Air pollution can cause acid rain, which

   contributes greatly to the problem of chemical weathering of statues, monuments, and so forth.

   _____

   _____

Going Further

Test some other substances to see how surface area affects their rate of chemical weathering. Obtain an iron nail and an equal mass of steel wool. Place each in an equal amount of water. Carefully observe the amount of rusting that takes place over several days.

_____ *Laboratory Investigation* _____

Investigating the Composition of Soil

You may want to refer students to pages J120–J126 in their textbook for a general discussion of soil formation and composition.

Time required: 40 minutes

Background Information

All of the soil on the Earth was formed by the weathering of parent rock material. Organic matter in the form of humus that was added to the uppermost portion of the soil produced a rich, dark-colored topsoil. Centuries of rainfall carried materials downward from the topsoil, where they were trapped in the lower regions of the soil and produced subsoil.

In this investigation you will observe samples taken from the topsoil, subsoil, and parent material near where you live. You will study the characteristics of these samples to learn more about the processes that produced the soils in your area.

Problem

Of what is soil made?

Materials *(per group)*

samples of topsoil, subsoil, and
    parent material
magnifying glass
teasing needle
small test tube with stopper
sheet of white, unlined paper
metric ruler

Topsoil and subsoil can be easily dug from the ground. Use crushed rock as parent rock material. The soil samples should be in containers. Use baby food jars or plastic sandwich bags.

Procedure

1. Using your ruler, draw two square shapes side by side on the sheet of unlined paper. Make each square approximately 5 cm on a side. Label one square "Topsoil" and the other square "Subsoil."

2. Place a small quantity of topsoil and subsoil on the sheet in the appropriate square. Instruct students to use approximately one teaspoonful of each.

3. Carefully observe the soil particles through the magnifying glass. Use the teasing needle to separate the particles. In the Data Table, list all characteristics of the topsoil and subsoil you can observe. Include such properties as color, particle size, and presence or absence of humus.

4. Carefully observe the sample of parent material, both with and without the magnifying glass.

5. You have learned that rainwater carries tiny soil particles downward from the topsoil into the subsoil. Many of the particles are too small to be seen with the unaided eye. These particles are called colloids. There is a simple test to detect colloids in soil. Place a small sample of soil, approximately a teaspoonful, in a test tube. Add water until the tube is about half-full. Place the stopper securely in the opening and shake the contents vigorously. Stop shaking the tube and allow the contents to settle for 2 or 3 minutes. If colloids are present, they will be so small that they will not settle quickly. They will give the water a cloudy look. Test the subsoil and topsoil for the presence of colloids.

6. Carefully replace the unused portions of your samples and clean up your work area.

Observations

DATA TABLE

Characteristics of Topsoil	Characteristics of Subsoil
Answers will vary, but students should notice that the topsoil sample is darker. It contains organic material. Its particles are generally smaller than the particles of the subsoil.	

1. How did the color of the topsoil and subsoil compare? The color of the topsoil may vary from nearly white to light brown, dark brown, or black depending on the amount of decomposed organic matter present. The greater the decayed organic content, the darker the topsoil. Chemical changes in the minerals present are responsible for other colors. Iron may cause reddish or yellowish colors, while many other chemical salts are white. The upper part of the topsoil is usually darkest, because of a higher concentration of humus. The subsoil is generally not as dark, since it contains less humus. The subsoil also contains clay and leached out minerals.

2. a. Did you find pieces of organic material in any of the three samples?

Organic material should have been most obvious in the topsoil sample.

b. Which sample contained the most organic material? The topsoil sample.

3. a. Were there any pieces of minerals present in either of the two soil samples?

(Mineral particles will appear as small shiny pieces of various colors.) <u>Probably yes.</u>

b. Did you find any of the same minerals in the sample of parent material? <u>Answers will</u>

<u>vary.</u>

4. When you placed the soil samples in water and shook them, the particles should have settled in a particular order.

a. Which particles settled first? <u>The largest.</u>

b. Which particles settled last? <u>The smallest.</u>

c. Which particles did not settle? <u>The colloids.</u>

Analysis and Conclusions

1. In what ways is the parent material similar to the soil?

<u>The characteristics will be the same if the soil is residual soil.</u>

2. In what ways is the parent material different from the soil?

<u>If the soil is transported, there may not be any minerals in common.</u>

3. Did you find indications that there were colloids present in your samples of topsoil and

subsoil? Explain your answer. <u>Probably yes. When the soil samples were mixed with water, shaken</u>

<u>vigorously, and then allowed to settle, the colloids should have remained suspended for both the topsoil</u>

<u>and subsoil samples. Their presence is indicated by the cloudy nature of the water even after several</u>

<u>minutes of settling.</u>

4. In some locations, soils were not formed from the parent material below them. Instead, they were formed somewhere else and were carried to their present location by winds, running water, or glaciers. If your soils were formed somewhere else and transported to your area, they will probably not resemble the parent rock material from your location. Based on your observations, do you think your soil formed from local parent material, or was it formed somewhere else and transported to your area? On what evidence do you

base your answer? <u>Answers will vary.</u>

Dynamic Earth   J ■ 55

Critical Thinking and Application

1. How does soil texture relate to weathering? Large soil particles, such as gravel, have been exposed to less weathering than smaller soil particles, such as sand, silt, and clay. The amount of weathering a material undergoes determines the particle size.

2. What do you think is responsible for the differences in color found in topsoil samples collected from various parts of the United States? Color differences can occur because of varying amounts of humus found in soil samples and because of different chemical contents. Iron tends to produce reddish or yellowish soil, while salts produce light-colored soil.

3. Is it possible to artificially increase the fertility of topsoil in a certain area? Explain your answer. A substance such as a fertilizer, which is rich in humus, can be used to artificially increase the fertility of topsoil.

4. In which of the four climatic regions—arid, semiarid, subhumid, humid—would you expect to find the richest topsoil? Explain your answer. A humid environment should produce the richest topsoil. Humidity increases the decomposition rate of plant and animal remains that form the humus in the topsoil. A greater amount of humus will produce a richer topsoil.

Going Further

Test several different types of soil in your neighborhood or around the school. For example, collect soils from places that are particularly sandy or rocky. Repeat the above investigations using the soils that you collect.

_____ *Laboratory Investigation* _____

Weathering and Soil Formation

12

A Closer Look at Soil

You may want to refer students to pages J123–J126 in their textbook for a general discussion of soil composition.

Time required: 40 minutes plus periodic follow-up for a week

Background Information

Billions of kilograms of topsoil wash toward the ocean every year. Much of the erosion results from human actions, such as cutting down forests, allowing animals to graze too much, and growing one crop over and over in the same field.

When topsoil is lost, agriculture suffers. But the loss of topsoil has another important effect. It upsets the delicate balance between living things and natural resources. Many species of living things make the soil their home. Without soil, these organisms and their contributions to other living things disappear from a region.

In this investigation you will discover what organisms are present in soil.

Problem

What kind of plant and animal life can be found in a sample of topsoil and subsoil taken from ground near your school?

Materials *(per group)*

small hand shovel or digging tool
6 plastic bags, with elastic or
   wires for closing
3 paper cups
3 paper plates
white tray or large sheet of
   white paper
small sieve
microscope

medicine dropper
microscope slides and coverslips
magnifying glass
forceps
12 to 16 small glass jars with lids
clean sand
30 radish seeds or other fast-germinating
   seeds (soaked overnight in water)
metric ruler

You may need to spend several minutes reviewing with your students the correct method of handling and using a microscope.

Procedure

1. Decide as a class where to look outdoors for soil samples.

2. Your group should collect a sample of soil about 30 × 30 × 30 cm. Use a metric ruler to measure the plot. Then dig down to about 60 cm and take another small sample.

3. Notice the differences between topsoil and subsoil. Pack the samples into six plastic bags. Seal and number the bags. Record the depth, texture, and moisture of the soil in each plastic bag in the Data Table.

4. In the classroom, carefully examine the soil. Use the sieve over the tray or white paper to separate organisms. Record the number of each type of organism you find. Place each organism in a glass jar. Be sure to add a small amount of the soil in which the organism was found. Observe the organisms carefully over the next few days.

🧪 **5.** Make several slides of soil samples for observation under a microscope. Each time you place small bits of soil on a glass slide, use the medicine dropper to add a drop of water to the sample. Cover the slide with a coverslip. Look under the microscope for protists, algae, and bacteria. Review with your students the correct way to handle and use a microscope, and the correct preparation of a slide.

6. Place soil samples from different depths on the plastic plates. Moisten the samples with water. Place some by the window. Observe the samples for several days.

7. Place sand in one cup, topsoil in another cup, and subsoil in a third cup. Label the cups appropriately. Plant 10 radish seeds in each cup. Be sure to spread the seeds apart and to lightly water the soil. Observe the cups for several days.

Observations

DATA TABLE

Bag Number	Depth	Texture	Moistness	Organisms Observed
1				
2				
3			Answers will vary.	
4				
5				
6				

1. How many centimeters thick was the layer of topsoil?

Answers will vary depending on the location.

2. How did the texture of the soil at the surface differ from the texture at 60 cm?

The soil at the surface contains more humus, is less densely packed, and is more porous.

3. How many kinds of living things did you find in the topsoil?

Answers will vary.

4. What does each living thing use for food? Answers will vary. Some predator-prey relationships
may appear.

5. How many kinds of living things did you find 60 cm deep?

Expect not to find many organisms here.

6. Describe living things that appeared on the plates after about a week.

Mosses, molds, and seedlings might be seen.

Analysis and Conclusions

1. Did you find more organisms living closer to the surface or deeper in the soil? How can you explain this observation? Students should have found more organisms living closer to the surface of the soil, where there is a more abundant supply of nutrients, moisture, and oxygen.

2. Did the radishes grow better in topsoil or in subsoil? How can you explain this observation? Probably in the topsoil. In the topsoil it is easier for roots to penetrate, there are more nutrients, and more oxygen can get to the roots.

3. When the topsoil erodes from a field, what would you expect to grow in the field? Very little. Crops will not grow when the topsoil has eroded away.

Critical Thinking and Application

1. Why are living organisms important in maintaining fertile topsoil? Living organisms help break apart large pieces of soil as they burrow, produce acids which chemically break down rocks, and produce humus when they die and decay.

2. In addition to the organisms you found in this investigation, list three other organisms that live in the soil. Answers will vary depending on the organisms the students found in the laboratory, but may include earthworms, ants, gophers, moles, mice, beetles, and so forth.

3. Lumber companies will now replant forest areas after cutting down the trees originally found there. How does this help reduce the problem of soil erosion?

The newly planted trees help to shield the topsoil from rainwater or wind, which can carry it away.

4. Many people who live directly on the coast have their homes built up on stilts that are deeply buried in the sand. Is there a practical reason for this? Explain your answer.

Ocean waves can erode the coastline. Houses sitting up on stilts are less affected by shifts in the soil

than houses that are sitting directly on the sand. Also, stilts protect a house from high water levels

produced by storms.

Going Further

A soil's particular chemistry determines what type of vegetation will grow in it. For example, a soil can limit vegetation growth if it is too acidic or basic. Test a sample of the topsoil and subsoil you collected with a few drops of 2% litmus solution in order to determine your soil's pH.

2% litmus solution can be prepared by mixing 2 g of powdered litmus with 98 mL of water.

Laboratory Investigation

Erosion and Deposition

13

Using a Stream Table

You may want to refer students to pages J140–J143 in their textbook for a general discussion of erosion caused by running water.

Time required: 40 minutes per day for two days

Background Information

A very effective device for examining erosion, deposition, and transportation of sediments is a stream table. You can make a stream table using a flat wooden, or molded plastic, seed tray from a nursery or by making your own.

To make a stream table, use a piece of thin plywood, 100 cm × 65 cm × 2 cm. Nail small pieces of wood, 10 cm × 2.5 cm, around the plywood base. Make a small opening at one end of the stream table and insert a piece of rubber tubing. This will allow water to drain into a catch bucket. Waterproof the stream table by caulking around the base and sides or use a plastic trash bag to line the inside. You can run a hose from a sink or use a siphon from a pail as a source of water. The hose should have a spray nozzle. A watering can can also be used to simulate "rainfall."

In this investigation you will use a stream table to investigate running water and erosion. You will notice stream wandering, undercutting, deltas, deposits, and other features.

Problem

How can a stream table be used to investigate the effects of running water on the land?

Materials *(per class)*

stream table
sand
gravel
wooden block, 4 cm × 10 cm
buckets
hose with spray nozzle or a sprinkling can

Procedure

1. Obtain a moist mixture of sand and gravel that is sufficient to cover the bottom of the stream table to a depth of about 1.5–2.0 cm. Place the mixture in the stream table, leaving an area at the bottom empty. You can create some surface features such as hills, valleys, and so on. Using a wooden block, raise one end of the stream table slightly. See Figure 1.

2. At the raised end of the table, lightly spray the surface from a water source, such as a sprinkling can or hose with a spray nozzle connected to the sink. This water source represents "rainfall." Observe the stream patterns that develop. Draw an aerial view of the stream pattern in the space provided in Observations.

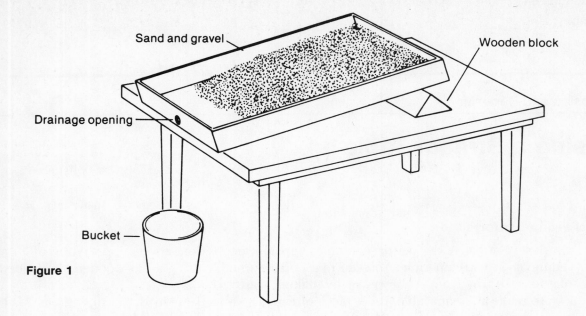

Sand and gravel

Wooden block

Drainage opening

Bucket

Figure 1

3. After the water has drained out, draw the material that has been carried down the "stream" and deposited at the mouth of the stream in the space provided in Observations. Be sure to note where the large pebbles have been carried and where the small sand grains have been deposited.

4. Arrange the sand and gravel in the stream table as in step 1. This time raise the stream table at one end to double the height.

5. Lightly spray the water as in step 2. Once again draw the aerial view of the "stream" and an aerial view of the "delta" and deposited materials in the space provided in Observations.

6. Draw a small part of the "stream" along a straight section and along a curved section in the spaces provided in Observations.

Observations

Raised end

Aerial View of Stream Pattern

Raised end

Aerial View of Delta and Deposited Material

Raised end

**Aerial View of Stream Pattern and Delta
(Slope Increased)**

**Straight Section
of Stream**

**Curved Section
of Stream**

Analysis and Conclusions

1. What effect does the steepness of the slope have on the stream pattern?

   As the steepness of the slope increases, the stream pattern becomes straighter. The steeper slope also cuts the river bed deeper.

2. What effect does the steepness of the slope have on the amount of material carried by the stream? A steeper sloped stream will carry more sediment.

3. If a dam were placed across the "stream," what would you notice?

   The water would slow down upstream from the dam. Sediment would be deposited near the dam.

4. What difference do you notice between the sections of the stream that are straight and those that are curved? The curved portion shows erosion on the outside part of the curve and deposition on the inside portion.

Critical Thinking and Application

1. Old rivers have a tendency to meander. Explain why this happens.

   As a river or stream runs, it tends to curve because it undercuts the bank on the outside and deposits sediment on the inside. This causes the stream to curve even more.

2. How do you think ground cover, such as trees or grass, would affect the rate of erosion produced by a stream? Ground cover would act to slow down the amount of erosion produced by a stream.

3. Why do streams carry more soil and rock material during a flood than during regular times? A flooding stream moves faster and has a greater volume than a normal stream. Therefore, it is capable of carrying more soil and rock material.

4. If the rainfall were the same in both areas, do you think runoff would be greater in a warmer climate or a cooler climate? Explain your answer.

In a warmer climate, there would be more evaporation of water and more vegetation to reduce runoff.

Therefore, runoff would be greater in a cooler climate.

5. Would you classify the Colorado River, which runs through the Grand Canyon, as an old or a young river? On what evidence would you base your answer?

Due to the tremendous amount of erosion that has occurred in the Grand Canyon, the Colorado River would be considered an old river.

Going Further

Use the stream table to investigate the effects of a melting glacier. Mix 1 L of sand and gravel with 500 mL of clay and water in a cake pan. Freeze the mixture until solid. Remove the pan from the freezer and place it on the raised portion of the stream table. Write a report explaining what happens as the "glacier" melts.

_____ *Laboratory Investigation* _____

14

Observing Sediment Deposition in Quiet Water

You may want to refer students to pages J134–J154 in their textbook for a general discussion of erosion and deposition.

Time required: 40 minutes

Background Information

As flowing streams and rivers empty into ponds and lakes, they carry with them bits and pieces of rock and soil. These small particles are known as sediment. Sediment begins when the processes of weathering act on the materials that make up the Earth's crust.

When the waters that carry sediment flow into a body of quiet water, such as a lake, various things can happen to the particles that make up the sediment. Some of them settle to the bottom of the lake almost immediately; others take much longer. Some particles may take years to settle out. Still others become dissolved in the lake water and never sink to the bottom.

In this investigation you will construct a model body of water and observe how sediment is deposited on the bottom.

Problem

How do differences in size and density of particles affect the length of time it takes for the particles to settle in quiet water?

Materials (*per group*)

3 plastic columns   Available from any science equipment supply house.
3 rubber stoppers for columns
timer   Use second hand of wall clock if necessary.
ring stand
2 burette clamps
sand particles of different sizes   A mixture of sandbox sand and fish-tank gravel works well.
equal-sized particles of different density   Glass boiling beads and "BBs" or lead shot are the same size but different density.

Procedure
Part A Particle Size and Settling Time

1. Insert a rubber stopper into a plastic column. Use the clamps to set up the apparatus as shown in Figure 1. Add water to the plastic column until it is about three-quarters full.

2. Examine the sand particles of different sizes. Record the relative sizes of the particles, from largest to smallest, in Data Table 1.

3. Drop a pinch of the largest sand particles into the column. Record the time it takes for most of the particles to reach the bottom in Data Table 1. Disregard any particles that float on the surface. Drop a second pinch of large sand particles and again record the time they take to reach the bottom in Data Table 1.

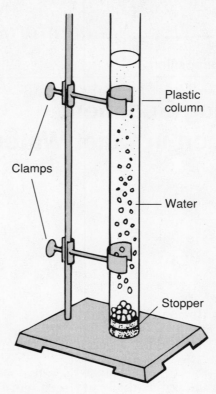

Plastic column

Clamps

Water

Stopper

Figure 1

4. Repeat this procedure for each size sand particle. Calculate the average settling time for each particle size. Record it in the proper space in Data Table 1.

Part B Particle Density and Settling Time

1. Remove the plastic column and set it aside. Attach another plastic column fitted with a rubber stopper. Fill the column three-quarters full with water.
Instruct students how best to discard the column of water in your particular lab setting.

2. Gather equal-sized particles of different density. Glass beads and BBs have been provided. Record their relative density, from higher to lower, in Data Table 2.

3. Determine the settling time for the different particles. To do this, determine the settling time for one sample of each density and then repeat the procedure. Record these results in Data Table 2.
Emphasize that students must drop the particles one at a time.

4. Calculate the average settling time for samples of each different density and record your results in Data Table 2.

Part C Settling Pattern of Mixed Particles

1. Remove the plastic container and set it aside. Insert another plastic container fitted with a rubber stopper into the apparatus and fill it three-quarters full with water.

2. Drop a handful of sand particles of different sizes into the column. Let them settle to the bottom.

3. Carefully observe the nature and extent of the sorting out of particles as they collect on the bottom of the column. In Figure 2 of Observations, sketch what you see in detail.

Observations

DATA TABLE 1   Answers will vary. However, the larger particles will settle first.

Relative Particle Size	Trial 1	Trial 2	Average Time
Largest			

DATA TABLE 2

Particle Type	Relative Density	Trial 1	Trial 2	Average Density
	Higher			
	Lower			

Density of glass is about 5.3 g/cm³. Density of steel BBs is about 7.5 g/cm³.

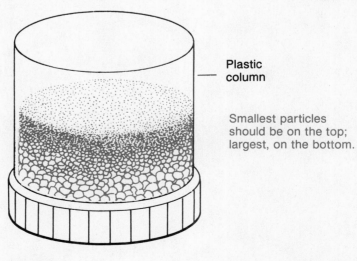

Plastic column

Smallest particles should be on the top; largest, on the bottom.

Figure 2

Analysis and Conclusions

1. What effect does size have on the length of time it takes for particles of sediment to settle in quiet water? The larger the particle, the less time it takes to settle.

2. What effect does density have on the length of time it takes for particles of sediment to settle in quiet water? The greater the density, the less time it takes to settle.

Critical Thinking and Application

1. If particles of different sizes are dropped into quiet water, describe the order in which they would settle. The largest particles settle first. The smallest particles settle last, on top of the larger ones.

2. An observer reported that she found large particles of sand deposited on top of smaller particles in a sample of sediment. Give a possible explanation for her discovery.

   The sample might have been overturned or the smaller particles might have been more dense than the larger particles and thus have settled first. For example, metallic sands are far more dense than granitic sands.

Going Further

Devise an experiment to determine the effect of size and density on particle deposition in running water. Perform the experiment. How do your results compare to the results of this investigation?